LARGE PRINT CROSSWORDS

LARGE PRINT CROSSWORDS

This edition published in 2020 by Arcturus Publishing Limited
26/27 Bickels Yard, 151–153 Bermondsey Street,
London SE1 3HA

ISBN: 978-1-78888-396-2
AD006640UK

Printed in China

1

Across

1 Domesticated relative of the llama (6)

7 Clergyman ministering to an institution (8)

8 Filled with wonder (4)

10 Portray (6)

11 Basic unit of currency in France (4)

13 Monastery (5)

14 Spectacles (7)

16 Earnest attempt at persuasion (3,4)

17 Bicker (5)

19 Give out (4)

21 Consortium of companies formed to limit competition (6)

23 Ms Amos, songstress (4)

24 Person who doubts the truth of religion (8)

25 Mass departure (6)

Down

1 Largest cartilage of the larynx (coll) (5,5)

2 Having patches coloured differently (4)

3 Harsh or corrosive in tone (5)

4 Terrestrial, material (7)

5 London thoroughfare associated with journalism (5,6)

6 Fibber (4)

9 Pleasure and delight (11)

12 Branch of medicine that deals with childbirth (10)

15 Mollify (7)

18 Elegance and beauty of movement (5)

20 Prefix meaning a million (4)

22 Output of a power plant (4)

2

Across

4 Creative person (6)
7 Manual worker (8)
8 Watchman (6)
9 Cot (4)
10 Fatal disease of cattle (inits) (3)
12 Instruction (5)
13 Out-of-date person or thing (coll) (3-4)
16 Recurrent rhythmical series, beat (7)
18 Beam used to support floors (5)
21 Employ (3)
22 Male pig (4)
23 Hindu Festival of Lights (6)
25 Aid to memory (8)
26 Reduce in rank (6)

Down

1 More impartial (6)
2 Sleeping place for two people (6,3)
3 Make illegal payment in exchange for favours (5)
4 London football club (7)
5 Bronzing of the skin caused by the sun (3)
6 Scratch repeatedly (6)
11 Having the capacity to soak up liquids (9)
12 Imaginary monster or ogre (3)
14 Hard-shelled fruit of a tree (3)
15 Come into possession of (7)
17 In operation (6)
19 Humiliated (6)
20 Limited periods of time (5)
24 Fuss (3)

3

Across

1 Gait (4)

3 Fearless daring (8)

9 Sporting dog (7)

10 Fruit with yellow flesh (5)

11 Detrimental to health (12)

14 Cut part of a tree trunk (3)

16 Muslim name for the one and only God (5)

17 Two performers (3)

18 Balderdash, piffle (6-6)

21 Asian country (5)

22 Abandon (7)

23 Delighted (8)

24 Clubs used in the game of cricket (4)

Down

1 Capable of happening or existing (8)

2 Gambling game using two dice (5)

4 Address of a page on the World Wide Web (inits) (3)

5 Oval large stadium with tiers of seats (12)

6 Take legal possession of, confiscate (7)

7 Sailing vessel with two masts (4)

8 Object used in playing a popular table game (8,4)

12 Swelling, protuberance (5)

13 Filleted (8)

15 Former unit of currency in the Netherlands (7)

19 Plays, theatre (5)

20 Cut back on certain foods (4)

22 Adversary (3)

4

Across

1 Diadem (5)
4 Thrive, do well (7)
8 Large body of salt water (3)
9 Assign (5)
10 Discolour (5)
11 Loose protective coverall worn over clothing (6,4)
13 Silvery metallic element (6)
15 Dairy product (6)
18 Retiring, not arrogant (10)
22 Complacently foolish (5)
23 Genetic copy (5)
24 Bird similar to an ostrich (3)
25 Crush by treading heavily (7)
26 Moves in large numbers, swarms (5)

Down

1 Tutoring (8)
2 Make an off-the-cuff remark (2-3)
3 With legs stretched far apart (7)
4 Small padded envelope (6)
5 Band that featured Liam and Noel Gallagher (5)
6 Nutty sweet (7)
7 Basic unit of money in South Africa (4)
12 Unnecessary and unwarranted (8)
14 Musical setting for a religious text (7)
16 Coiffure (7)
17 Elasticated rope (6)
19 Slumber (5)
20 Fumble (5)
21 Combat between two mounted knights (4)

5

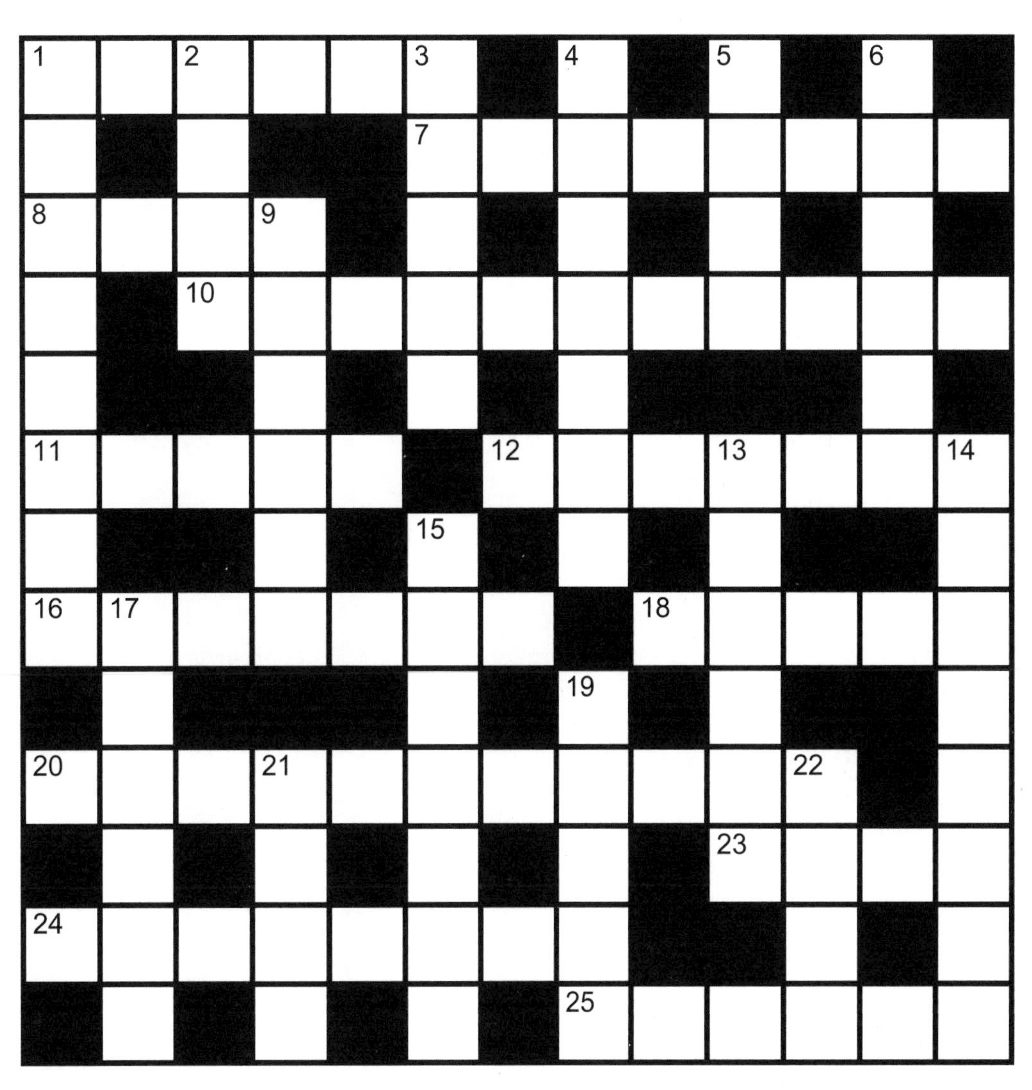

Across

1 Light glass formed on the surface of some lavas (6)

7 Fragrant (8)

8 Hard fruits (4)

10 Trader who sells sewing and dressmaking materials (11)

11 Aromatic edible bulb (5)

12 Padded cloth covering to keep a pot warm (3,4)

16 Unexpected piece of good fortune (7)

18 Chocolate powder (5)

20 Having a body temperature that is internally regulated (4-7)

23 Yugoslavian leader who died in 1980 (4)

24 Coalition (8)

25 Sudden flash (as of lightning) (6)

Down

1 Table tennis (4-4)

2 Nocturnal flying creature (4)

3 Consumed (5)

4 Member of an army (7)

5 Feline animals (4)

6 Dots on a computer screen (6)

9 Beauty establishments (6)

13 Clothes cupboard (6)

14 Reference work published annually (8)

15 Lean towards (7)

17 Shrine where a god is consulted (6)

19 Hemispherical roofs (5)

21 Female domestic (4)

22 Nearly hopeless (4)

6

Across

1 Cloth dolls worn on the hand (5,7)

9 Opaque gems (5)

10 Cocktail fruit (5)

11 Prompt (3)

12 Lariat (5)

13 Abatement (7)

14 Examine (6)

16 Hidden or undeveloped (6)

20 Gather what a person says by watching his or her mouth move (3-4)

22 Fleshy root (5)

24 Gaming cube (3)

25 France's longest river (5)

26 Oval fruit with a very large seed (5)

27 Musician in an orchestra (12)

Down

2 Those who cannot tell the truth (5)

3 Sticky, syrupy (7)

4 Particularly difficult or baffling problems (6)

5 Puddles (5)

6 Large imposing building (7)

7 Prospect (5)

8 Small indefinite quantity (6)

15 Copy (7)

17 Endeavour (7)

18 Extreme fear (6)

19 Advance evidence for (6)

20 Mauve-flowered shrub (5)

21 Resin used in aromatherapy (5)

23 Component parts of a skeleton (5)

7

Across

1 Make unhappy (6)
7 Capital of Indonesia (7)
8 Four-wheel covered carriage (6)
10 Grip of a tyre on a road (8)
12 Breakfast food (6)
15 Rental contract (5)
16 Vessel for travel on water (4)
17 Decapod crustacean (4)
18 Get the better of (5)
19 Gas found in air (6)
22 Areas where vehicles may be left temporarily (3,5)
23 Accompany (6)
25 Night attire (7)
26 Data input device for computers (6)

Down

1 Capital of Oregon, USA (5)
2 Classroom fool (5)
3 Long and distinct period of history (3)
4 Common wild bird of North America (6,5)
5 War-whoop (6,3)
6 Abel's brother (4)
9 Practical, unpretentious (11)
11 Of a sphere, flattened at opposite sides (6)
13 Imaginary place considered perfect (6)
14 If one may use that expression (2,2,5)
20 Bring together, assemble (5)
21 Observed (5)
22 Cloak-like garment (4)
24 Office of a bishop (3)

8

Across

1 Dreadful (7)
8 Inner whorl of petals in a flower (7)
9 Falls on the Canada/US border (7)
10 Draw forth (6)
12 Association of sports teams (6)
14 Printing from a plate with raised characters (11)
19 Connect (6)
22 Snooze (6)
25 Stays in place (7)
26 Gastronome (7)
27 Mobile home (7)

Down

1 Object on which an item of clothing is placed (6)
2 Form a mental image (7)
3 Giraffe-like creature (5)
4 Confidence trick (4)
5 Unlawful act (5)
6 Scarf bandage (5)
7 Keg, cask (6)
11 Biting tools (5)
12 Ran easily (5)
13 One of four playing cards in a deck (3)
15 Popular beverage (3)
16 Factory in which timber is cut into planks, etc (7)
17 Woven floor covering (6)
18 Spring that spouts hot water (6)
20 Bone in the leg (5)
21 Hit hard (5)
23 Cuban dance (5)
24 Worry excessively (4)

9

Across

4 Get in touch (7)
8 Belonging to them (5)
9 Form of transport (9)
10 Everyone except the clergy (5)
11 Factory where workers do piecework for poor pay (9)
13 Pleasure obtained by inflicting harm on others (6)
16 Make unauthorised alterations (6)
20 Make merry (9)
23 Civilian clothing (5)
24 Native Australian (9)
25 Audacity (5)
26 Own (7)

Down

1 Slanted letters (7)
2 Made up one's mind (7)
3 Unravels due to friction (5)
4 Foundation garment (6)
5 Volatile liquid used chiefly as a solvent (7)
6 Cause to feel self-conscious (5)
7 Truss (3,2)
12 Poem intended to be sung (3)
14 Yes (3)
15 Worthy of adoration or reverence (7)
17 Likes better (7)
18 No longer active in one's profession (7)
19 Sleeping compartments on a ship (6)
20 Hold firmly in the arms or hands (5)
21 Loud-roaring animals of the cat family (5)
22 Make corrections to (5)

10

Across

1 Marked by uncontrolled excitement or emotion (7)
5 Solid building material (5)
8 Manipulate in a fraudulent manner (3)
9 Cause to conform to a standard (9)
10 Gives the cry of an ass (5)
11 Make warm (4)
13 Subdued colour (5)
15 Clear space in an area of woodland (5)
16 Popular house plant (5)
18 Ingenuous (5)
19 Ship's company (4)
21 Partially melted snow (5)
22 Decapitating (9)
23 Hatchet (3)
24 Shed tears (5)
25 Of the greatest possible degree (7)

Down

1 Arsonist (7)
2 Make worse (9)
3 Metallic element used to make light-bulb filaments (8)
4 Abundant gas (6,7)
6 Cultivated land (5)
7 Put (pressure) on (5)
12 Inspire with confidence (9)
14 Vision (8)
17 Gain with effort (7)
19 Three-dimensional (5)
20 In what place? (5)

11

Across

1 State of deep-seated ill-will (6)

4 Unbroken mustang (6)

9 Country, capital San José (5,4)

10 Control a vehicle (5)

11 Utter intentions of harm towards (8)

13 Young newt (3)

14 Vegetable matter used as a fuel (4)

15 Go out with (4)

16 Open area of grassy land (3)

19 Drink (8)

21 Extended area of land (5)

23 Make free from bacteria (9)

24 First light (6)

25 ___ butter, popular spread (6)

Down

1 Stir up (6)

2 Mean person (5)

3 Reckless and impetuous person (8)

5 Peruse text (4)

6 One put forward for election (7)

7 Countries of Asia (6)

8 Vital organ of the body (5)

12 Imaginary standard by which things are measured (8)

14 Fuss, commotion (7)

16 European country (6)

17 Country, capital Sana'a (5)

18 Smallest in number (6)

20 Person born under the sign of the Ram (5)

22 Russian monarch (4)

12

Across

1 Act well or properly (6)
4 Church official (6)
7 Drink made of wine mixed with sparkling water (8)
8 Grassy garden area (4)
9 Stage item (4)
10 Incongruous, inviting ridicule (6)
12 Warns of danger (6)
15 Military group (4)
17 Maori war dance (4)
18 Royal personage (6)
19 Generator (6)
22 Material effigy worshipped as a god (4)
23 Succulent plant (4)
24 Make uniform or matching (8)
25 Rubs out, obliterates (6)
26 Lines directed to an audience (6)

Down

1 Make a strenuous effort (coll) (4,1,3)
2 Adversity (8)
3 Elector (5)
4 Flummoxed (9)
5 Ensnare (4)
6 Units of scoring in cricket (4)
8 Reluctant (5)
11 Intrepid, resolute (9)
13 Having a regular wage (8)
14 Female hereditary title (8)
16 Commerce (5)
20 Periods of time (5)
21 Overdue (4)
22 US mid-western state (4)

13

Across

1 Disease of cattle and sheep (7)
4 Engrave (5)
7 Concentrated (7)
8 Marsh bird of the heron family (7)
9 Have a meal (3)
10 Ship equipped to detect and destroy explosive devices (11)
14 Antisocial misdeed by a minor in violation of the law (11)
18 Expend (3)
19 Hair cleanser (7)
20 Marked by great enthusiasm (7)
21 Glacial (5)
22 Renders unable to hear (7)

Down

1 US 'Heart of Dixie' state (7)
2 Scottish plaid (6)
3 Reaches maturity (6)
4 Perennial herb also known as nepeta (6)
5 Participant in a race (6)
6 Special occasion (5)
7 City in northern Scotland (9)
11 Film starring Bette Davis, All about ___ (3)
12 Good discernment (3)
13 Very wealthy or powerful businessmen (7)
14 Particular (6)
15 British political party (6)
16 Country, capital Kampala (6)
17 Teat (6)
18 Decompress a compressed file (5)

14

Across

1 Censure severely or angrily (6)

4 Protective covering on a boot or shoe (6)

9 Projectile (7)

10 Stylistic talent (5)

11 Zero (3)

12 Look at intently (5)

13 Capacious (5)

15 Stay clear of (5)

16 Attitude, beliefs (5)

18 Salt water (5)

20 Holy sister (3)

21 Throbbed dully (5)

22 Dead and rotting flesh (7)

23 Group of countries with one ruler (6)

24 Wind off from a spool (6)

Down

1 Cause to be confused emotionally (6)

2 Organised study (8)

3 Two times (5)

5 Set down (7)

6 Crop pouch of a bird or insect (4)

7 March in a procession (6)

8 Disposition to do good (11)

14 Displaying acceptance or certainty (8)

15 Into pieces (7)

16 Hire for service (6)

17 Aromatic herb (6)

18 British peer of the lowest rank (5)

19 Strip of fried potato (4)

15

Across

1 Stand-in doctor (5)

4 Person who cuts and sets panes into windows or doors (7)

8 Bring about (7)

9 Biblical shepherd who slew Goliath (5)

10 Centre (5)

11 Matrimonial (7)

12 High-kicking dance of French origin (6)

13 Expressing in words (6)

16 Speak unfavourably about (7)

18 Burn (5)

20 Valuable quality (5)

21 Wearing away (7)

22 Physician who performs operations (7)

23 Gloomy and drab (5)

Down

1 Dog's lead (5)

2 Opening move, preliminary event (7-6)

3 Small or minor detail (7)

4 Lubricating substance (6)

5 Supplement (3,2)

6 Inquiry into questionable activities (13)

7 Danger signal (3,4)

12 Short, curved sword (7)

14 Leave without permission (7)

15 Belittle (6)

17 Remove a knot (5)

19 Fop (5)

16

Across

1 Game in which hidden articles must be found (8,4)

8 Less than the correct or full amount (5)

9 Hawaiian wreath (3)

10 Hours between evening and morning (5)

11 Golf course by the sea (5)

12 Guard (8)

15 Stubbornly persistent in wrongdoing (8)

17 Commercial exchange (5)

20 Deviating from the truth (5)

21 Scots 'no' (3)

22 Primitive plant forms (5)

23 Mayonnaise dressing often served with fish (7,5)

Down

1 Popularising a fashion (5-7)

2 Stylish and graceful (7)

3 Provide with nourishment (7)

4 Person who handles equipment for travelling bands (6)

5 Boarding-house for holidaymakers (5)

6 Man-made material (5)

7 Motor that burns heavy oil (6,6)

13 Central part of an atom (7)

14 Arctic deer with large antlers (7)

16 Carnivorous burrowing mammal (6)

18 Scene of action (5)

19 Raise in rank, character, or status (5)

17

Across

1 Cycle rickshaw (7)

6 Beast of burden (3)

8 With the extremity facing the observer (3,2)

9 Meets a want or need (7)

10 Immediate (7)

11 Transported in one's arms (7)

13 Breakfast food (6)

15 Periodical that summarises the news (6)

18 Characterised by strong feelings (7)

19 Adhesive tape used in dressing wounds (7)

21 Marine fowl (7)

22 In Hinduism, an ascetic holy man (5)

23 H Rider Haggard novel (3)

24 Saunters (7)

Down

2 Train (7)

3 Crook (8)

4 Abreast of (6)

5 The ___ of March, 2011 film (4)

6 Moderately slow tempo in music (7)

7 Athletic competition in which a heavy metal ball is hurled (4,3)

12 Extinct reptile (8)

13 Direction indicator (7)

14 Regress (7)

16 Quite a few (7)

17 Against (6)

20 Periodic rise and fall of sea level (4)

18

Across

1 Inhabitant (8)

5 High in stature (4)

9 Dealers (7)

10 Radioactive gas (5)

11 Small adhesive tokens stuck on letters or packages (7,6)

12 Wept convulsively (6)

14 Humorously sarcastic (6)

17 Sloping surface on which washed dishes are put to dry (8,5)

19 Forms a layer over (5)

20 Of a fabric made from the hair of sheep (7)

21 At another time (4)

22 Volcanic island in Indonesia (8)

Down

1 Eight-armed creature (7)

2 Packs to capacity (5)

3 State of being ready, especially against attack (12)

4 Embedded (6)

6 Belly (7)

7 Loans out (5)

8 Periodic lack of inspiration afflicting authors (7,5)

13 Bluster (7)

15 Brilliant solo passage near the end of a piece of music (7)

16 Solution (6)

17 Russian country house (5)

18 Distribute (5)

19

Across

1 Fruit of a thorny shrub (7)
5 Military fabric (5)
8 Ringlets (5)
9 Skeletal structure (7)
10 Impulse, whim (7)
11 Foundation (5)
14 Swirled round and round (6)
17 Not awake (6)
22 Be important (5)
25 Metal container in which coal or charcoal is burned (7)
26 Perpetual (7)
27 Asian water lily (5)
28 Dentist's assistant (5)
29 Harsh or unfair treatment (coll) (3,4)

Down

1 Use again after processing (7)
2 Banded, streaked (7)
3 Antagonistic (7)
4 Hold discussions with an enemy (6)
5 Skewered meat dish (5)
6 Natives of Kuwait, for example (5)
7 Objects (5)
12 Sicken (3)
13 Frost (3)
15 Twosome (3)
16 Hostelry (3)
18 Lacking depth (7)
19 Long, formal letter (7)
20 Sun umbrella (7)
21 Maltreater (6)
22 Dirt-free (5)
23 Cow's milk-gland (5)
24 Subject (5)

20

Across

1 Scallywag (6)

4 Small pleasure boat powered by cycling (6)

7 Ornamented evergreen used as a seasonal decoration (9,4)

11 Relating to the heart (7)

12 Capital of Senegal (5)

13 Perform (3)

14 Imbecile (5)

15 Japanese monetary unit (3)

16 Andean mammal (5)

17 Self-possession (7)

19 Small and intermittent amounts (coll) (5,3,5)

23 Gives way (6)

24 Rain-bearing cloud (6)

Down

1 Contest of speed (4)

2 22nd letter of the Greek alphabet (3)

3 Allow (3)

4 Pulse vegetable (3)

5 Magic word used in a spell or in conjuring (11)

6 Short musical drama (8)

8 Ordinary members of an organisation (4,3,4)

9 Undertaker (9)

10 In a prompt or rapid manner (7)

11 Draws back, as with fear or pain (7)

12 Occurring or done regularly (3-2-3)

18 Requests (4)

20 Public promotions (abbr) (3)

21 Ask for overdue payment (3)

22 Male sheep (3)

21

Across

1 Remains in place (5)

4 Picks out (7)

8 Cereal grass (3)

9 Protective covering for the front of a machine or device (9)

10 Max ___, German artist (1891–1976) (5)

11 Pardoned (7)

13 Person who manages or directs (13)

15 Book part (7)

17 Hits with an open hand (5)

19 Occurring every third year (9)

21 Brother of George Gershwin (3)

22 Disinfect, sterilise (7)

23 Crustlike surfaces of healing wounds (5)

Down

1 Ambit (5)

2 Word opposite in meaning to another (7)

3 Means of protection from injury, hardship, etc (6,3)

4 Government department concerned with espionage (6,7)

5 Rim (3)

6 Edible shellfish (5)

7 Slim or small (7)

12 Pupa (9)

13 Practitioner of rigorous self-discipline (7)

14 Russian empress (7)

16 Line spoken by an actor to the audience (5)

18 Scorches (5)

20 Granny (3)

22

Across

1 Eastern marketplace (6)

7 Popular frozen dessert (3,5)

8 Hard outer layer of a fruit (4)

10 Secret or hidden (6)

11 Second Greek letter (4)

12 Group of eight (5)

14 Made of clay (7)

16 Far away (7)

17 Grove of trees (5)

20 Bath powder (4)

21 Service of china or silverware, used at table (3,3)

23 Fury (4)

24 Make-believe (8)

25 Disturbed the public peace (6)

Down

1 World's third largest island (6)

2 Bluish-white metallic element (4)

3 Traveller on horseback (5)

4 In the middle (7)

5 Someone undergoing a trial period (11)

6 Ability of a dye to maintain its colour (8)

9 Make docile and tractable (11)

13 Quality of a knight (8)

15 Becoming as one (7)

18 Surpass (6)

19 Creator (5)

22 Diplomacy (4)

23

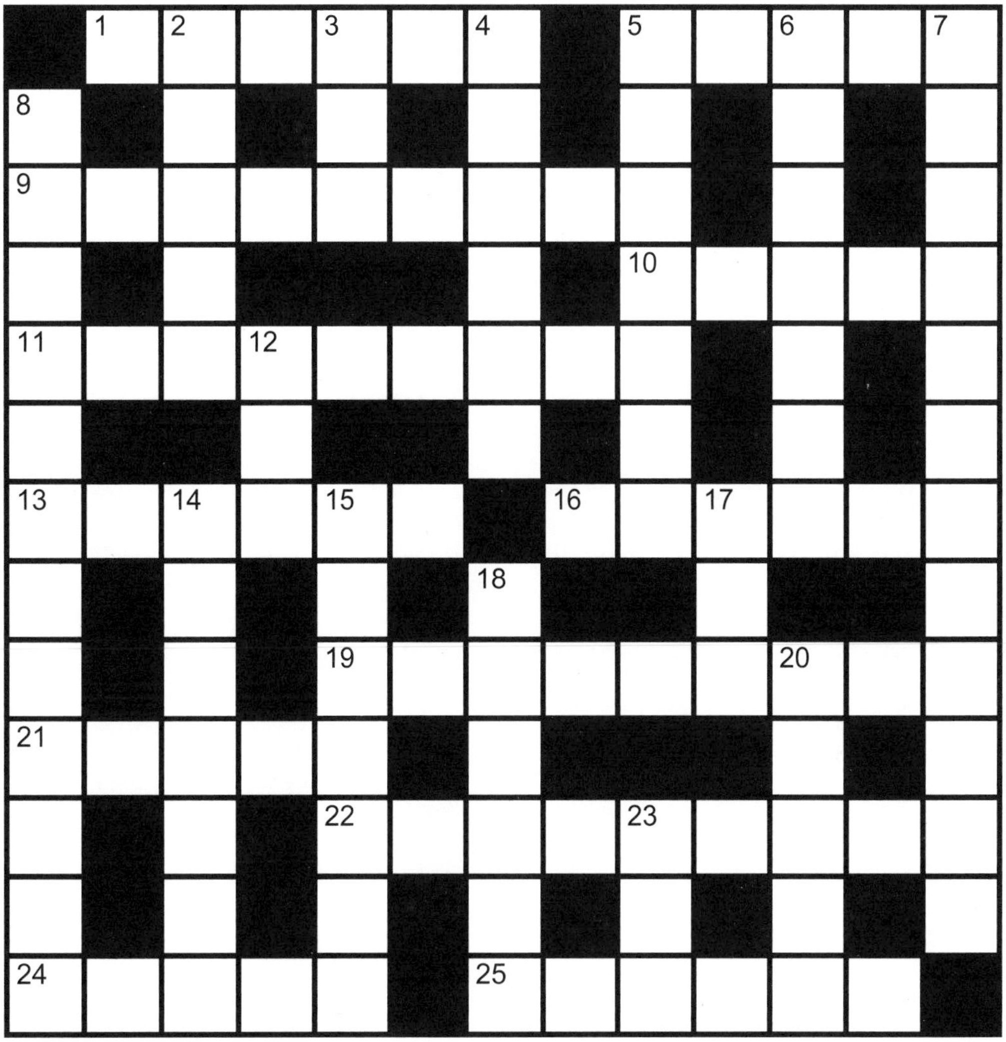

Across

1 Acid found in vinegar (6)

5 Make appear small by comparison (5)

9 Sparkling citrus fruit drink (9)

10 Tower supporting high-tension wires (5)

11 Light, canvas gym shoes (9)

13 Arrangement (6)

16 Migratory game fish (6)

19 Unable to be heard (9)

21 Things that must not be done, said, etc (coll) (2-3)

22 Book containing a list of synonyms (9)

24 Kitchen range (5)

25 Popular spice (6)

Down

2 American raccoon (5)

3 Trail, track (3)

4 Baby's bed (6)

5 Relating to the lowest parts of the ocean (4-3)

6 Enthusiastic approval (7)

7 One of the gifts brought by the Wise Men to Jesus (12)

8 Having full control of one's mind (6,6)

12 Rug (3)

14 Person deemed contemptible (2-3-2)

15 Long, formal letter (7)

17 Hawaiian floral garland (3)

18 Pitch dangerously to one side (6)

20 Carried (5)

23 Law passed by Parliament (3)

24

Across

1 In a difficult situation (2,3,4)
7 Feed (3)
8 Mixed feelings or emotions (11)
11 Supernatural (7)
12 Illegal setting of fires (5)
15 Transfer one's right to (6)
16 Climb (6)
18 Embrace tightly in one's hands (5)
21 Manages with what is available (5,2)
22 Feeling of annoyance or anger (11)
25 To stretch out (3)
26 Superiority over another (9)

Down

1 Reproductive cells (3)
2 Metal ring that opens a can (3)
3 Not circulating or flowing (8)
4 The Friendly Islands (5)
5 Depends on (5)
6 Knocked unconscious by a heavy blow (7)
9 Subtraction sign (5)
10 Slanted letters (7)
13 Childhood disease caused by a deficiency of vitamin D (7)
14 Slow Cuban dance and song in duple time (8)
15 Defendant in a criminal proceeding (7)
17 Lowest point (5)
19 Tree with rot-resistant wood (5)
20 Tagliatelle or ravioli, for example (5)
23 Country (inits) (3)
24 Before, poetically (3)

25

Across

1 Involuntary vibration (6)

7 One who administers a test (8)

8 Baby's bed (4)

10 Reckoning (11)

11 Large bird of prey (5)

12 Act like a mirror (7)

16 Disperse (7)

18 Cud-chewing mammal of desert regions (5)

20 Digit situated next to the thumb (5,6)

23 Vessel made of wooden planks (4)

24 Light brown raw cane sugar (8)

25 Reduced to pulp (6)

Down

1 Insensitive (8)

2 Large-scale (4)

3 Arrive at (a destination) (5)

4 At a previous point in time (7)

5 Cut back on certain foods (4)

6 Showing extreme courage (6)

9 Vote (6)

13 Person who inspires others (6)

14 Endowed with natural abilities (8)

15 Piece of cloth attached to a pole, used to signal danger (3,4)

17 Sign of the zodiac (6)

19 Remove a lid (5)

21 Fencing sword (4)

22 Contest of speed (4)

26

Across

1 Summarise briefly (5)

5 Vessel for travel on water (4)

7 Expression of sorrow (2,4)

8 Formal school balls held at the end of a year (5)

9 Respected leader in national or international affairs (9)

10 Flushed (3)

11 Collection of live animals for study or display (9)

15 Functioning competently (9)

19 Automobile (3)

20 Formal expression of goodwill (9)

21 Chinese secret society (5)

22 Dissimilar (6)

23 Charitable gifts (4)

24 Semi-liquid (5)

Down

1 Adroitness and cleverness in reply (8)

2 Nebulous (6)

3 Arboreal marsupial (6)

4 Hold back (8)

5 Cut of beef from the chest (7)

6 Compound capable of turning litmus blue (6)

12 Entitled, qualified (8)

13 Commonplace (8)

14 Inciting sympathy and sorrow (7)

16 Conventional (6)

17 Sample (6)

18 Lawsuit (6)

27

Across

1 Underground cemetery (8)
5 Feat (4)
7 Proficient (5)
8 War vessel (7)
9 Hawaiian wreath (3)
10 Tropical fruit with a yellow skin and pink pulp (5)
11 Unit of heat, often applied to a foodstuff (7)
13 Smugly complacent (4-9)
20 Put down by force or intimidation (7)
22 Pungent edible bulb (5)
23 Listening organ (3)
24 Hide from view or knowledge (5,2)
25 Humble (5)
26 Held back, retained (4)
27 Anonymous (8)

Down

1 Fuel formerly used for heating and lighting (4,3)
2 Foot digit protector (7)
3 Short, curved sword (7)
4 Sorcery (5)
5 Leave abruptly (4,3)
6 Building (7)
12 Muhammad ___, former boxer (3)
14 Small opening through which one can look (7)
15 Ardent, keen (7)
16 Public promotions (abbr) (3)
17 Depository for goods (7)
18 Copy (7)
19 Perils (7)
21 Rich brown pigment (5)

28

Across

1 Canter (4)

3 Daughter of a sovereign (8)

7 Railway buildings (8)

8 In one's sleeping place (4)

9 Improve in quality (6)

11 Small active songbird (6)

12 Respond to a stimulus (5)

13 Gasps for breath (5)

15 Attractively old-fashioned (6)

17 First light (6)

19 Roman cloak (4)

20 Come into view once more (8)

21 Minor celestial body composed of rock and metal (8)

22 Podium (4)

Down

1 Bunch of cords tied at one end (6)

2 Transmitting live from a studio (2,3)

3 Authoritative person who divines the future (7)

4 Gusset (5)

5 One who extracts fuel from a pit (9)

6 On the Origin of ___, work by Charles Darwin (7)

10 Lifeless (9)

12 Rowdy, strident (7)

13 Sign carried during a demonstration (7)

14 Large northern marine mammal (6)

16 Main part of the human body (5)

18 Last letter of the Greek alphabet (5)

29

Across

1 Fetched (7)
5 Savoury jelly (5)
8 Experimenting until a solution is found (5,3,5)
9 Compère (coll) (5)
11 Breathe (7)
13 Frightened (6)
14 Assorted, diverse (6)
17 Colourless liquid obtained from coal (7)
18 Aladdin's spirit (5)
19 Set of automatic signals for controlling vehicles (7,6)
22 Craggy, mountainous (5)
23 Cul-de-sac (4,3)

Down

1 Takes the trouble (7)
2 Kimono sash (3)
3 First James Bond film in which Pierce Brosnan starred (9)
4 Period of occupancy (6)
5 Playing card (3)
6 Vertical structure that divides or separates (9)
7 Cut into slices (5)
10 Flexible armour made of interlinked metal rings (5,4)
12 Place of complete bliss (7-2)
15 Clothed (7)
16 Fought with épées (6)
17 Collection of cakes, for instance (5)
20 English actress and recipe author, ___ Ripley (3)
21 Garden tool (3)

30

Across

1 Rear-facing point on an arrow (4)
3 Site (8)
9 Member of an army (7)
10 Showy garden plant (5)
11 Detail considered to be insignificant (12)
14 Recede (3)
16 Develop fully (5)
17 Travel on the piste (3)
18 Glowing (12)
21 Young bird (5)
22 Hangs around (7)
23 Elementary particle with a negative charge (8)
24 Computer memory unit (4)

Down

1 Infatuated (8)
2 Remnant of the past (5)
4 Rowing pole (3)
5 Popular song on New Year's Eve (4,4,4)
6 Driving force (7)
7 Number represented by the Roman IX (4)
8 Semi-formal evening wear for a man (6,6)
12 Managed (5)
13 Aversion (8)
15 Outdoor blaze (7)
19 ___ board, used to shape fingernails (5)
20 Throb dully (4)
22 ___ Tolstoy, writer (3)

31

Across

1 Griddle cake (7)
5 Facial hair (5)
8 Owns (3)
9 Most direct route (7)
10 Drive out (5)
11 Spiny plants (5)
13 Economic aid in the form of a grant (7)
15 Revised before printing (6)
16 Bring a shine to (6)
19 Acute intestinal infection (7)
20 Jordanian monetary unit (5)
21 Less than the correct or full amount (5)
23 Unwanted discharge of a fluid (7)
25 Lyrical poem (3)
26 Protect from light (5)
27 Lockjaw (7)

Down

1 Booth (7)
2 Purpose (3)
3 Honour (9)
4 Belief in the existence of God (6)
5 Fatal disease of cattle (inits) (3)
6 Cold-blooded vertebrate (9)
7 Postpone (5)
12 Small thin sausage (9)
14 Cause to become widely known (9)
17 Restraining straps (7)
18 Case for holding money (6)
19 Prices (5)
22 Pedal digit (3)
24 Stiff bristle on an ear of rye (3)

32

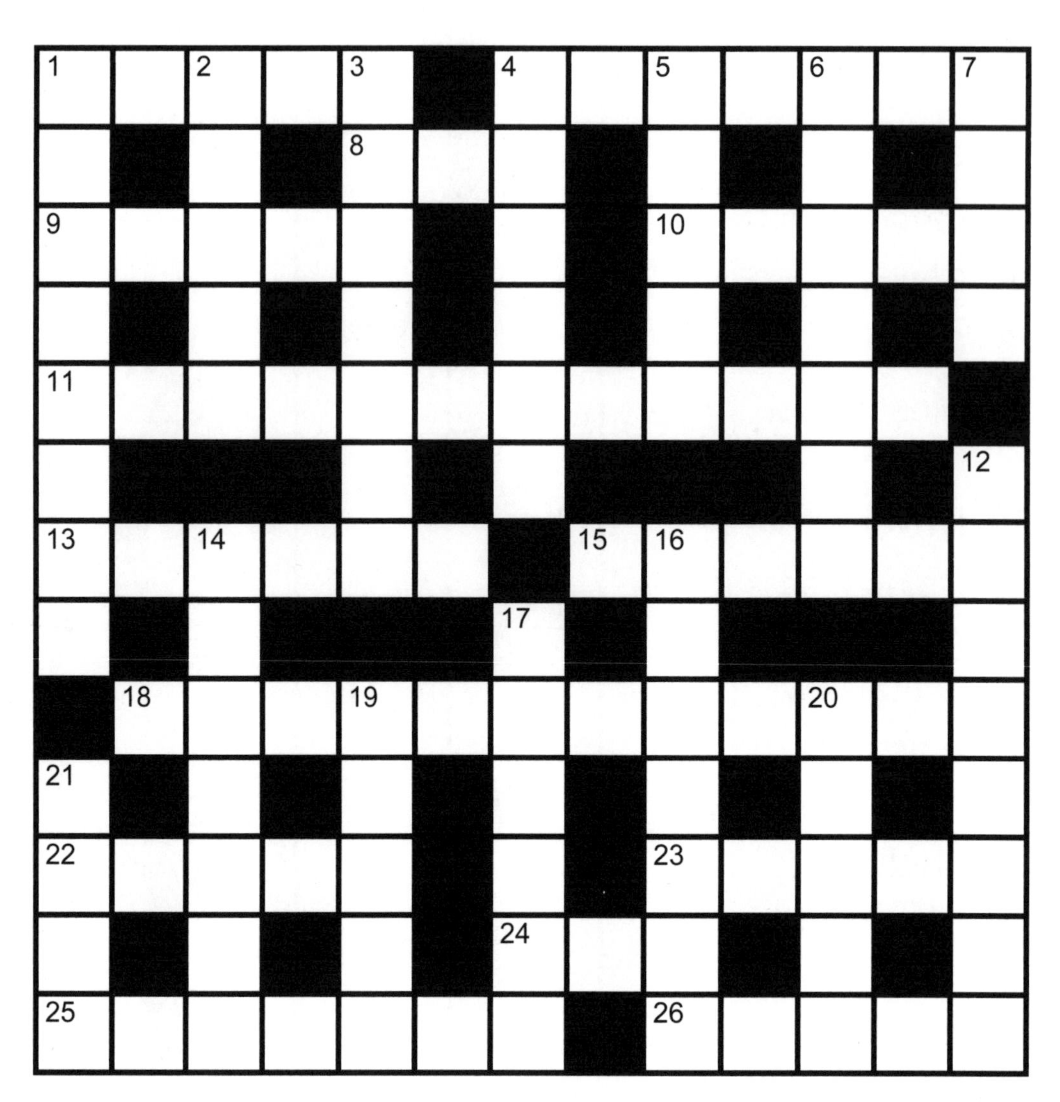

Across

1 Proportion (5)
4 Formal military gestures (7)
8 Show displeasure vocally (3)
9 Potatoes (coll) (5)
10 Main artery (5)
11 Orchestrated (a complex operation) (12)
13 Having decayed or disintegrated (6)
15 Bloodsucking African fly (6)
18 Depriving of confidence or enthusiasm (12)
22 Per ___, for each year (5)
23 Coconut meat (5)
24 Chopping tool (3)
25 Marked with stripes (7)
26 Exchanges for money (5)

Down

1 Fragrant herb (8)
2 Violent young criminals (5)
3 Designed to incite to indecency (7)
4 Grave, dignified in manner (6)
5 Commit to memory (5)
6 Extreme suffering (7)
7 Unwanted email (4)
12 Natives of Antwerp, for example (8)
14 More slender (7)
16 Spiritualists' meetings (7)
17 Expenditure (6)
19 Punctuation mark (5)
20 Force (5)
21 Flexible containers for shopping (4)

33

Across

4 City in western Israel (3,4)

8 Non-professional (7)

9 Mixer drink (5)

10 Walt Disney film of 1941 (5)

11 Large open vessel for liquids (3)

12 Bingo (5)

13 Expanse of scenery (9)

17 Indigestion (9)

21 Maxim ___, Russian playwright (5)

22 Which person? (3)

23 Remove the fleece from (5)

24 Crowd actor (5)

25 Disperses, sprawls (7)

26 Daybreak (7)

Down

1 Crane fly (coll) (5-4-4)

2 Pub employee (6)

3 Lures (6)

4 Unimportant details (6)

5 Minuscule (6)

6 Excessive pride (6)

7 British military decoration for gallantry (8,5)

14 Weep (3)

15 Small hard seed found in some fruits (3)

16 United Kingdom native (6)

17 Hindu Festival of Lights (6)

18 Marriage partner (6)

19 Make certain of (6)

20 Children's outdoor toy (6)

34

Across

1 Female pantomime character (4)

3 Person who does no work (8)

9 Person of equal rank, status or ability (7)

10 Seat (5)

11 Simple (5)

12 Distilled alcoholic beverages (7)

13 Fable (6)

15 Insist (6)

18 Serious (7)

19 Diadem (5)

21 Musical entertainment (5)

22 Containing too many words (7)

23 Writer of literary works (8)

24 Heating elements in an electric fire (4)

Down

1 Unit of relative loudness (7)

2 Contagious viral disease (5)

4 Transversely (6)

5 Profession of designing buildings (12)

6 Musical toy (7)

7 Gets weary (5)

8 Celebration of a 300th anniversary (12)

14 Growing areas (7)

16 Boxlike containers in a piece of furniture (7)

17 Lines on which musical notes are written (6)

18 Wear away by natural forces (5)

20 Hawaiian greeting (5)

35

Across

1 Swore (6)

5 Bass instruments of the violin family (6)

8 Imitates (4)

9 Slaughterhouse (8)

11 Having weapons (5)

12 Holy war (7)

15 Person or organisation that is influenced or controlled by another (6)

16 Relating to the stars (6)

18 Concentration (7)

20 Scottish lakes (5)

22 Reply of denial (8)

24 Melt (4)

25 Stroke tenderly (6)

26 Male relative (6)

Down

2 Relating to capital letters (5,4)

3 Temporarily prevent from continuing (7)

4 Pull, haul (4)

5 President of a board of directors (8)

6 Asian water lily (5)

7 Judo belt (3)

10 Fish eggs (3)

13 Speed by which the population declines (5,4)

14 Image boosts (3,5)

17 Ballroom dance in double time (3-4)

18 Cacophony (3)

19 Bring dishonour upon (5)

21 Incline (4)

23 Long and distinct period of history (3)

36

Across

1 Against the direction of the breeze (6)
5 Home for a hog (6)
8 Filleted (8)
9 Very docile (4)
10 Light brown (3)
11 Small area of still water (4)
13 Too, as well (4)
14 Closed political meeting (6)
15 Handle (4)
17 Weedy annual grass (4)
18 Tree with sharp thorns (6)
19 Professional charges (4)
20 Curved structure (4)
21 Owned (3)
22 Cattle reared for their meat (4)
23 Diminished in strength or quality (8)
25 Clement ___, former PM (6)
26 Former Spanish monetary unit (6)

Down

2 Authoritative declaration (13)
3 Perfect (5)
4 Expire (3)
5 Nut with an edible green kernel (9)
6 Athlete (7)
7 Storage box filled with valuables (8,5)
12 Raincoat material (9)
16 Coy, shy (7)
20 Pseudonym (5)
24 Drivel, trash (3)

37

Across

1 Uttered aloud (4)
3 Example (8)
9 Taste experience (7)
10 Small, open pies (5)
11 Country, capital Cairo (5)
12 Violent effort (6)
14 Extend in one or more directions (6)
16 Less tame (6)
18 Turn into (6)
19 Telling fibs (5)
22 Natives of Kuwait, for example (5)
23 Family appellation (7)
24 All people (8)
25 Sleeping places (4)

Down

1 Experienced pain (8)
2 Country, capital Rome (5)
4 Small group of words expressing a single concept (6)
5 Butterfly or moth larvae (12)
6 Wed (7)
7 Bird's construction (4)
8 Without ceasing (12)
13 Advance (8)
15 Make ready (7)
17 Human being (6)
20 Mental representation (5)
21 Cook in an oven (4)

38

Across

1 Music genre (9)
6 Feline mammal (3)
8 Girl's name (5)
9 Reduce to small shreds (5)
10 Equine animal (3)
11 Distribute (5)
12 Place in concealment (7)
13 Country, capital Bujumbura (7)
19 Feeling or showing love (7)
21 Judder (5)
22 Beverage (3)
23 Fool (5)
24 Separated into pieces (5)
25 Acquire (3)
26 Unanimity (9)

Down

1 High-kicking dance (6)
2 Mythological god of light and day (6)
3 Treatment of symptoms by applying pressure with the fingers to specific points (7)
4 Examine (a witness) minutely and persistently (5-8)
5 Reasoned judgment (5)
6 Alpine summer residence (6)
7 Layered (6)
14 Injure permanently (7)
15 Housing or outer covering (6)
16 Basic unit of money in Hungary (6)
17 Small, lightweight boats (6)
18 Area set back or indented (6)
20 Relating to sight (5)

39

Across

1 Sickness (6)

8 Level above which ice remains permanently (4,4)

9 Long, narrow passageways (6)

10 Lifting device (8)

11 Against (6)

13 Formed, fashioned (6)

16 Concluding (4)

18 Red eruption of the skin (4)

19 Listener (6)

20 University city (6)

23 Plodding (8)

25 Characteristic pronunciation (6)

26 Faith (8)

27 Peevish (6)

Down

2 Stand, endure (5)

3 Goes into a huff (5)

4 Valuer, estimator (8)

5 Short, light sleep (4)

6 Visible speck that drifts across the eyeball (7)

7 Pledged to be married (9)

11 Done of one's own free will (9)

12 Sudden forceful flow (4)

14 Haughty (8)

15 Lower part of an interior wall (4)

17 Plant's climbing organ (7)

21 Aspect (5)

22 Cattle farm (5)

24 Coloured part of the eye (4)

40

Across

3 Lampoons, ridicules (9)
8 Depart, go (5)
9 Authorise use of medicine (9)
10 Minutes (5)
11 Opposite in nature or effect (7)
13 King with a golden touch (5)
15 Take without permission (5)
16 Titles (5)
20 Factions (5)
22 Usually (2,1,4)
23 Repeat performance (5)
24 Indefensible (9)
25 Moves towards (5)
26 Food turner with a broad blade (4,5)

Down

1 Popular children's party game (9,4)
2 Remained in readiness for a purpose (6)
3 Invasion by pathogenic bacteria (6)
4 A dozen (6)
5 Happens again (6)
6 Party of people assembled in the evening (6)
7 Insomnia (13)
12 Eye infection (4)
14 Top cards (4)
17 Insect that rests with forelimbs raised as if in prayer (6)
18 Canonised people (6)
19 City formerly called Bombay (6)
20 Calm, unagitated (6)
21 Marked by the appetites and passions of the body (6)

41

Across

1 Despatches (5)

7 One of the three superpowers in Nineteen Eighty-Four (7)

8 Direct (3)

9 Adaptable (9)

11 Drama which is sung (5)

12 Mr Bonaparte (8)

16 Forms a mental picture (8)

20 Inadvertent incorrectness (5)

21 Onlooker (9)

23 Division of an ocean (3)

24 Unspecified person (7)

25 Loop formed in a cord (5)

Down

1 Impose a blockade on (4,3)

2 Digit, quantity (6)

3 Related to wooded regions (6)

4 Sneering look (4)

5 Leopard (7)

6 Light-beam intensifier (5)

10 Teatime sweet bread roll (5)

13 Relating to birds (5)

14 Workers' dining hall (7)

15 Land area, especially of a farm (7)

17 Discourse (6)

18 Wall painting (6)

19 Bottomless gulf or pit (5)

22 Feat (4)

42

Across

1 Meddlesome (4)

3 Unmelodious (8)

9 Relating to the country of which Ankara is the capital (7)

10 Noisy altercation (5)

11 Took an oath (5)

12 Trucks (7)

13 Gives instruction (6)

15 Is unable to (6)

17 Receive a share of (7)

18 Oozes (5)

20 Currently in progress (5)

21 Thor Heyerdahl's famous raft (3-4)

22 Short tube attached to the muzzle of a gun (8)

23 Peruse (4)

Down

1 Stage shows put on at Christmas (8,5)

2 Cornstalks (5)

4 Not hallowed or consecrated (6)

5 Causing to feel shame (12)

6 Dodging, non-payment (7)

7 Smugly complacent (4-9)

8 Preschool for very young children (12)

14 Disturbance, usually in protest (7)

16 Challenge aggressively (6)

19 Leave or strike out, as of vowels (5)

43

Across

1 One who looks after a sick relative (5)

4 Guru (7)

8 Little rascal (3)

9 Passage into a colliery (9)

10 Old Testament mother-in-law of Ruth (5)

11 Sycophants (7)

13 Money paid to named beneficiaries when policyholder dies (4,9)

15 Island group, ___ and Barbuda (7)

17 Popeye's girlfriend (5)

19 Narrow escape (4,5)

21 Fruit of a rose plant (3)

22 Detect with the senses (7)

23 Rustic (5)

Down

1 Mound of stones piled up as a memorial (5)

2 Expression of criticism and censure (7)

3 Staying on (9)

4 Appearance in bodily form, materialisation (13)

5 Possesses (3)

6 Faintly detectable amount (5)

7 Professional entertainer (7)

12 Person who promotes armed conflict (9)

13 Acquired knowledge (7)

14 Not one nor the other (7)

16 Catches (5)

18 Send or drive out (5)

20 Be equal, draw (3)

44

Across

1 Waxy animal substance used in perfume (9)

8 Milky-white gem (5)

9 Convex moulding with a cross section of a quarter of a circle (5)

10 Produces musical tones with the voice (5)

11 Cultivates by growing (5)

12 Sailors (6)

13 Money demanded by a kidnapper (6)

17 State of depression (5)

20 Draw a conclusion (5)

22 Flocks (5)

23 Eagle's nest (5)

24 Fictitious name (9)

Down

1 Buenos ___, capital of Argentina (5)

2 Sudden happening that brings good fortune (7)

3 Quick-witted retort (7)

4 Well-seasoned stew (6)

5 Parody (5)

6 Edge tool used in shaving (5)

7 Flower (7)

12 Quieted and brought under control (7)

14 Liquorice-flavoured herb (7)

15 Crocus stigmas used in flavouring food (7)

16 Outbuilding for housing a car (6)

18 Far beyond the norm (5)

19 Woolly ruminant (5)

21 Kingdom (5)

45

Across

1 Muslim form of salutation (6)

7 Commendation (8)

8 Donkey (3)

9 Ms Stone, aka Catherine Tramell in the Basic Instinct films (6)

10 Savoury meat paste (4)

11 Twilled woollen fabric (5)

13 Water tank (7)

15 Embarrassed (7)

17 Alloy of copper and zinc (5)

21 Placed in position (4)

22 To the opposite side (6)

23 In the month preceding the present one (abbr) (3)

24 Marked by excessive self-indulgence and moral decay (8)

25 Not including (6)

Down

1 Lines on which musical notes are written (6)

2 One who grants a tenancy (6)

3 Perform a wedding ceremony (5)

4 Outdoor (4-3)

5 Machine for performing calculations automatically (8)

6 Last thing mentioned (6)

12 Protector (8)

14 Discussed an issue (7)

16 Covered with a waterproof coating (6)

18 Take for granted (6)

19 Seven people considered as a unit (6)

20 Banal (5)

46

Across

1 Faint (4,3)

8 Archaeological period (4,3)

9 Involvement (7)

10 Join up (6)

12 Take up residence (6)

13 Your dad's dad! (11)

17 Turn up (6)

20 Young nobleman attendant on a knight (6)

23 Do away with (7)

24 Period that starts on 1 January (3,4)

25 Person whose job it is to dust and vacuum, etc (7)

Down

1 Mattress filled with straw (6)

2 Machine that inserts metal fasteners into sheets of paper (7)

3 Desert garden (5)

4 Cans (4)

5 Dome-shaped dessert (5)

6 Pursue like a ghost (5)

7 Insect's antenna (6)

11 Royal House (5)

12 Paving stones (5)

14 Issue of a newspaper (7)

15 Voice box (6)

16 Greek god of the west wind (6)

18 Move stealthily (5)

19 Church associated with a convent (5)

21 Citation (5)

22 Refuse of processed grapes, etc (4)

47

Across

4 Deliverer of mail (7)

7 Flat highland (7)

8 Murdered (5)

9 Subject (5)

10 ___ Lanka, country (3)

11 Large ladle (5)

12 Likely to spread and cause an epidemic disease (9)

14 Uneducated person (9)

17 Proportion (5)

18 Country, capital Washington DC (inits) (3)

19 Larva of an insect with incomplete metamorphosis (5)

21 Closes with a bang (5)

22 Wheedling, cajoling (7)

23 Final stages of an extended process of negotiation (7)

Down

1 Skewer for holding meat over a fire (4)

2 Identification tags (6)

3 Happening again and again, tediously (11)

4 Go in search of (6)

5 Hayfield (6)

6 Skittles (8)

8 Female to whom one is related by marriage (6-2-3)

12 Member of an ancient Jewish sect around the time of Christ (8)

13 Filament (6)

15 Subtle difference in meaning (6)

16 Record of events from personal knowledge (6)

20 In a lofty position (4)

48

Across

1 One who travels on the piste (5)
4 Precious gem (7)
8 Indistinguishable (9)
9 Fowl's perch (5)
10 Worship (9)
13 Mark of disgrace (6)
14 Countries of Asia (6)
16 First meal of the day (9)
19 Spew forth lava and rocks (5)
20 Set of steps (9)
22 Breastbone (7)
23 Garments of a jockey (5)

Down

1 Beetles considered divine by ancient Egyptians (7)
2 Thoughtless (13)
3 Indian side dish of yogurt and chopped cucumbers (5)
4 The night before (3)
5 Further (5)
6 Relating to building design (13)
7 Bob ___, singer noted for his protest songs (5)
11 Make appear small by comparison (5)
12 Public acts of violence and disorder (5)
15 Walks quietly (7)
16 Foundation (5)
17 Holy book of Islam (5)
18 Time of life between the ages of 13 and 19 (5)
21 Limb (3)

49

Across

1 Characteristic mental attitude (7)

7 Stout-bodied insect which produces a loud, chirping sound (6)

9 Gruelling (7)

10 Backbone (5)

11 Most important point (4)

12 Ring-shaped bread roll (5)

16 Overcome or allay (5)

17 Conceal (4)

21 Native of Muscat, for example (5)

22 Small mild-flavoured onion (7)

23 Move unsteadily, with a rocking motion (6)

24 Place where seafood is processed and sold (7)

Down

1 King or queen (7)

2 Necessary for relief or supply (7)

3 Beauty parlour (5)

4 Person who follows the latest trends and fashions (7)

5 Biblical shepherd who slew Goliath (5)

6 Creator (5)

8 Set up (9)

13 Bush with berries used to flavour gin (7)

14 Act in disregard of laws or promises (7)

15 Give evidence (7)

18 Compass point at 180 degrees (5)

19 Control board (5)

20 Gives one's support or approval to (5)

50

Across

1 US national game (8)

5 Settled a bill (4)

7 Derived from living matter (7)

8 Surgeon's pincers (7)

9 Country, capital Tallinn (7)

11 Hinged window sash (8)

14 Emphasised (8)

17 More mentally alert (7)

18 Allure or entice (7)

21 Arctic deer with large antlers (7)

22 Lilliputian (4)

23 Occurring or done regularly (3-2-3)

Down

1 Caramel brown (4)

2 Repositories (6)

3 Diameter of a tube or gun barrel (4)

4 Slacken (6)

5 Showy birds (8)

6 Announced publicly or officially (8)

10 Heavenly body (4)

11 Saw against the grain (of wood, for example) (8)

12 Infinite time (8)

13 If not, then (4)

15 Emotional wound or shock (6)

16 Travelled across the ice (6)

19 Clump (4)

20 City of Helen, whose face "launched a thousand ships" (4)

51

Across

1 Wispy white cloud (6)

7 One who administers a test (8)

8 Girl's name, a diminutive form of Margaret (3)

9 Formally accuse (6)

10 Bridge (4)

11 Bright and pleasant (5)

13 Sales slip (7)

15 Collection of electrical cells (7)

17 Acknowledge (5)

21 Ms Chanel, fashion designer (4)

22 Burns with steam (6)

23 Toy which can be made to spin (3)

24 Sense of concern or curiosity (8)

25 Exertion of force (6)

Down

1 Field on which a university's buildings are situated (6)

2 Area (6)

3 Become established (3,2)

4 New Testament book (7)

5 Velocity of a plane (8)

6 Patch up or renovate (6)

12 Abundant gas (8)

14 Joint of meat (7)

16 Quantity (6)

18 Gather or bring together (6)

19 Token of victory (6)

20 Fritter away (5)

52

Across

1 Inclined to show mercy (7)
5 Swivel (5)
8 Someone undergoing a trial period (11)
9 Inhibition or ban resulting from social custom (5)
11 Everlasting (7)
13 Deadly (6)
14 Former name of the Indian city of Chennai (6)
17 Maintain or assert (7)
18 Blackbird (5)
19 Document of credentials (11)
22 Cleave (5)
23 Line touching a curve (7)

Down

1 City housing the seat of government of a country (7)
2 Inflated pride (3)
3 Clarify the meaning of (9)
4 Cause to stumble (4,2)
5 Livestock enclosure (3)
6 Patina often seen on copper (9)
7 Item (5)
10 Relating to plants (9)
12 Extremely harsh (9)
15 Most noticeable or important (7)
16 Floating aimlessly (6)
17 Gateaux (5)
20 Common type of rodent (3)
21 Yes (3)

53

Across

1 Cut off with the teeth (4)

3 Child's model railway (5,3)

9 Extremely poisonous substance (7)

10 Circumvent (5)

11 Airfield without normal airport facilities (7,5)

14 Small drink (3)

16 Hindu religious teacher (5)

17 Indian state, capital Panaji (3)

18 Person or thing that is inferior or subordinate to another (4,8)

21 Fourth letter of the Greek alphabet (5)

22 Muslim (7)

23 Drink made of wine mixed with sparkling water (8)

24 Digestive juice secreted by the liver (4)

Down

1 Adverse reaction to some political or social occurrence (8)

2 US novelist, creator of Tom Sawyer (5)

4 Repent (3)

5 Incapable of being disentangled (12)

6 Removing hair with a razor (7)

7 Affectedly dainty or refined (4)

8 Government employee (5,7)

12 Clear space in an area of woodland (5)

13 Marine crustacean (8)

15 One who sneaks about (7)

19 Two-syllable feet in poetry (5)

20 Tots up (4)

22 US musician and record producer, former husband of Tina Turner (3)

54

Across

1 Experience of thinking that a new situation has occurred before (4,2)

8 Active supporter and advocate (8)

9 Show in a picture (6)

10 Watcher (8)

11 Be present at (6)

12 Fire-raiser (8)

16 Ultimate clients for which a thing is intended (3-5)

18 Relating to the system for delivering mail (6)

21 Feeling of intense dislike (8)

23 Nicotinic acid (6)

24 International organisation that cares for the sick in wartime (3,5)

25 Degree (6)

Down

2 Choose by a vote (5)

3 Come up (5)

4 In accord with the latest fashion (2-2-4)

5 Canine creatures (4)

6 Docking (7)

7 Postpones (6)

11 Adept (4)

13 Apprehension about what is going to happen (8)

14 Part of an animal (4)

15 Yokels, country bumpkins (7)

17 Pinned down (6)

19 Well turned-out (5)

20 Foreigner, stranger (5)

22 Put away for storage (4)

55

Across

1 Ceremony of religious worship (7)
7 Study of plants (6)
9 Skeletal muscle having three origins (7)
10 Strainer (5)
11 Distinctive and stylish elegance (4)
12 Stratum (5)
16 Masculine (5)
17 Circle of light around the sun (4)
21 Dog-like nocturnal mammal (5)
22 Budding (7)
23 Climbing palm of Sri Lanka (6)
24 Remuneration (7)

Down

1 Slide unobtrusively (7)
2 Advocate of political reform (7)
3 Marked with printing fluid (5)
4 Additional dose that makes sure the first was effective (7)
5 Light brown, nut-coloured (5)
6 Uses a keyboard (5)
8 Attacker (9)
13 Trailer equipped with living quarters (7)
14 Recurrent rhythmical series, beat (7)
15 Omen (7)
18 Coast (5)
19 Bands to tie or buckle around the body (5)
20 Exorbitant rate of interest (5)

56

Across

1 Capital of Costa Rica (3,4)
5 Walt Disney film of 1941 (5)
7 Ladder steps (5)
8 Reconstruct (7)
9 Educational institution (7)
10 Saline (5)
11 Be resistant to (6)
13 Maintenance (6)
18 Stripes (5)
20 Run or skip about briskly (7)
21 Cases to carry (7)
22 Victoria Beckham's former surname (5)
23 Piece of pipe which bends backwards on itself (1-4)
24 Sorrow (7)

Down

1 Windstorm that lifts up clouds of dust (7)
2 Designed to reduce or prevent sliding (3-4)
3 Molluscs from which pearls are obtained (7)
4 Deserved by one's efforts (6)
5 Throws away as refuse (5)
6 Take air in and out (7)
12 Lowly agricultural labourer (7)
14 Sign posted in a public place as an advertisement (7)
15 Make amends for, atone (7)
16 Groups of words forming the grammatical constituents of a sentence (7)
17 Things of value or usefulness (6)
19 Wobble (5)

57

Across

1 External forms (6)
4 Dictated (6)
7 Slaughterhouse (8)
8 Celebration of the Eucharist (4)
9 Language, jargon (5)
10 Substance that produces a fragrant odour when burned (7)
12 Lose freshness, shrivel (6)
13 Caused to stop (6)
15 Commonly accepted as true on inconclusive grounds (7)
18 Pulse (5)
20 Gruelling (4)
21 Quietly and steadily persevering (8)
22 Head cushion (6)
23 Tidy up (6)

Down

1 Gastropod with a spiral shell (5)
2 Versus (7)
3 Outgoing person (9)
4 British peer of the lowest rank (5)
5 Mass of eggs deposited by frogs (5)
6 Become wider (7)
11 Land along the edge of a sea (9)
12 Idolise (7)
14 Violently fast stream of water (7)
16 Great danger (5)
17 Present with an income (5)
19 Conducting stick (5)

58

Across

4 Large shrimp cooked in breadcrumbs (6)
6 Upright pole on which a hinged barrier is hung (8)
7 Popular flavour of soup (6)
8 Mentally healthy (4)
9 Gratuity (3)
11 Dissident (5)
12 Due to, on account of (7)
15 More decorative (7)
17 Not as many (5)
20 Soften by soaking in water (3)
21 Native of Bangkok, for example (4)
22 Repair or mend (especially shoes) (6)
23 Put under water (8)
24 Exile from a community or group (6)

Down

1 Roof of the mouth (6)
2 Respect (9)
3 Value (5)
4 Bung (7)
5 Indicates the direction of (6)
10 Geographical index or dictionary (9)
11 Branch of the British armed forces (inits) (3)
13 At all times, poetically (3)
14 Give new strength or energy to (7)
16 Mohair (6)
18 Go by (6)
19 Thrusting blows (5)

59

Across

1 Given false details (11)

7 Centre (3)

8 Calculating (9)

9 Pursuing for food or sport (7)

11 Shaped dough made from flour, water and egg (5)

14 Cheap showy ornament (6)

15 Stubbornly unyielding (6)

16 Embrace (5)

19 Instrument from which a person is executed by hanging (7)

21 Swing from side to side regularly (9)

23 Anger (3)

24 Act of restoring or compensation (11)

Down

1 Great merriment (5)

2 Gall (3)

3 Supported monetarily (8)

4 Study intensively, as before an exam (coll) (3,2)

5 Financial obligations (5)

6 Swindle, cheat (7)

10 Pipes (5)

12 Heavenly being (5)

13 Dreamer (8)

14 Idyllically rustic (7)

17 Change (5)

18 Walks with a slow heavy gait (5)

20 Lustre (5)

22 Gave permission (3)

60

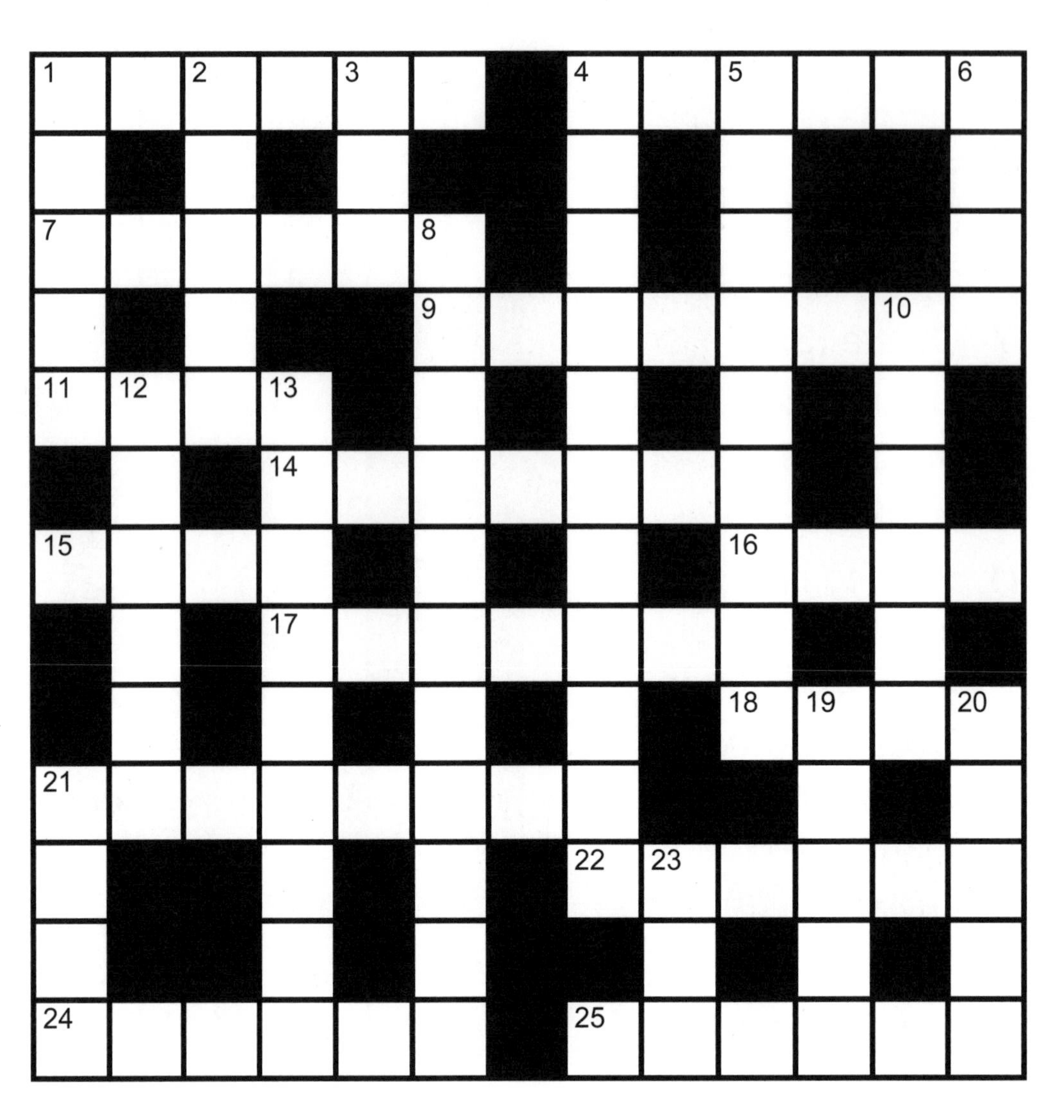

Across

1 Draw off liquid by atmospheric pressure (6)

4 Without much intelligence (6)

7 Marked by hardheaded intelligence (6)

9 Ardour (8)

11 Transparent optical device (4)

14 Coiffure (7)

15 Equipment for the reproduction of sound (2-2)

16 Territory (4)

17 Mollify (7)

18 Sketched (4)

21 Bird which forms large flocks at sunset (8)

22 Creamy alcoholic beverage (6)

24 Places a bet (6)

25 Puts off, discourages (6)

Down

1 Tiny (5)

2 Mountaineering spike (5)

3 Frequently, poetically (3)

4 Cheat someone by not returning enough money (5-6)

5 Still in doubt (9)

6 Confront with resistance (4)

8 Capable of producing an intended result (11)

10 Flinch, recoil (6)

12 Evoke (6)

13 Sunken vessel (9)

19 Wash off soap (5)

20 Earnings (5)

21 Solidifies (4)

23 Word of surprise (3)

61

Across

1 Goes into a huff (5)

7 Pass from the body (7)

8 ___ and buts, objections (3)

9 River, the boundary between Mexico and Texas, USA (3,6)

11 Fragment (5)

12 Newest, most immature (8)

16 Rhythmical songs traditionally sung by sailors (8)

20 Vile, despicable (5)

21 Absolve from blame for a fault or wrongdoing (9)

23 Hydrogen, for example (3)

24 Curled lock of hair (7)

25 Annoy continually (5)

Down

1 Sea captain (7)

2 Tilted to one side (6)

3 County in southern England (6)

4 Manufacturer of toy bricks (4)

5 Large wave falling on the shore (7)

6 Measuring device (5)

10 Class of artistic endeavour having a characteristic form (5)

13 Further from the centre (5)

14 Savage and excessive butchery (7)

15 Homer's epic poem (7)

17 Detective who follows a trail (6)

18 Crude or indecent (6)

19 Perceived sound (5)

22 Pretentious (4)

62

Across

1 Marked by intense agitation (6)

5 Involving financial matters (6)

8 Spherical in shape (6)

9 Meeting of spiritualists (6)

10 Law passed by Parliament (3)

11 Percolate (6)

13 Widow woman (7)

16 Nationalist (7)

17 Woolly-headed (6)

20 Tip of an ink pen (3)

21 Frayed (6)

22 Nonsense, ostentatious talking (6)

23 Gave a clue (6)

24 House of worship (6)

Down

2 Excitable (9)

3 Faith (5)

4 Durable aromatic wood (5)

5 Decorate with strings of flowers (7)

6 Malicious gossip (7)

7 Vegetable, emblem of Wales (4)

12 Uninterrupted in time (9)

14 Ideal future husband (2,5)

15 Suffering from physical injury (7)

17 Chief monk (5)

18 Material for jeans (5)

19 Curved shape that spans an opening (4)

63

Across

1 Sightless (5)

4 Obsolete (7)

8 Choose (3)

9 Police vehicles (5,4)

10 Take exception to (5)

11 Put out of action (by illness) (4,3)

13 Tills (4,9)

15 Volatile liquid used chiefly as a solvent (7)

17 Doomed Shakespearean lover (5)

19 Hand over to the authorities of another country (9)

21 Roman god of the sun (3)

22 Sound excluder (7)

23 Thick woollen fabric (5)

Down

1 Man with fair skin and hair (5)

2 Narrow strip of land connecting two larger land areas (7)

3 Common name for the jerboa (6,3)

4 System of windows with two panes of glass (6-7)

5 Distressing (3)

6 Cloak, often knitted (5)

7 Prevents deliberately from inheriting (7)

12 Rebel, guerrilla (9)

13 Acknowledge defeat (7)

14 All together, as a group (2,5)

16 Blue ___, flag indicating a ship is ready to sail (5)

18 Lubricated (5)

20 Sicken (3)

64

Across

1 Impersonate (5)
4 Poisonous metallic element (7)
8 Artificial human (7)
9 Evenly matched (5)
10 Fills to satisfaction (5)
11 Object formed by a mould (7)
12 Baldest (6)
13 Set of eight notes (6)
16 Played the leading rôle in (7)
18 Infectious disease (5)
20 Retired Argentinian professional footballer, ___ Maradonna (5)
21 In a perfect way (7)
22 Filled sack used to protect against floodwater (7)
23 Discernment (5)

Down

1 Water-filled ditches surrounding castles (5)
2 Large inland sea (13)
3 Picks out (7)
4 Advance evidence for (6)
5 Outstanding players in a tournament (5)
6 Units of length used in navigation (8,5)
7 Scented liquid (7)
12 In addition (7)
14 Remark (7)
15 Bordering (6)
17 Parallelogram with four equal sides (5)
19 Fashion (5)

65

Across

1 Fellow feeling (8)
5 At liberty (4)
9 The letter 'H' written as a word (5)
10 Horse's bit (7)
11 Not needing to be demonstrated or explained, obvious (4-7)
12 Plot of ground adjoining a house (6)
13 Amount of time (6)
16 Operate simultaneously (11)
17 Local language variant (7)
18 Edible organs (5)
20 Sight organs (4)
21 Secret phrase (8)

Down

1 Giving form to (7)
2 Coaster (3)
3 Seemingly small but actually mortal weakness (8,4)
4 Student lodging (6)
6 Without volition or conscious control (9)
7 Perpendicular (5)
8 Film stars who are adored blindly and excessively (7,5)
11 Amount of contraction (9)
14 Blinded temporarily (7)
15 Wealthy heiress in Shakespeare's The Merchant of Venice (6)
16 Grasslike marsh plant (5)
19 To and ___ (3)

66

Across

1 Measured the duration (5)

4 It's said to make the heart grow fonder (7)

8 Play featuring singing and dancing (7)

9 Growing older (5)

10 Cherished desire (5)

11 Conjunction expressing a doubt or choice between alternatives (7)

12 In a fearless and daring way (6)

13 Recollection (6)

16 Wax lighting rods (7)

18 Arch (5)

20 Combination of musical notes (5)

21 Investigate (7)

22 Least difficult (7)

23 Informal term for a father (5)

Down

1 Faint-hearted (5)

2 Sundry (13)

3 Maths system based on tens (7)

4 Lets (6)

5 Look at intently (5)

6 Immediate vicinity (13)

7 With keen anticipation (7)

12 Pedalled vehicle (7)

14 Broke loose (7)

15 Facet (6)

17 Home of a beaver (5)

19 Opposing military force (5)

67

Across

1 Member of the armed forces who does not participate in fighting (3-9)

9 Decompress a compressed file (5)

10 Force (5)

11 Manage (3)

12 Move furtively (5)

13 Christian recluse (7)

14 Take into custody (6)

16 French port city on the Loire (6)

20 Say out loud for the purpose of recording (7)

22 Cleave (5)

24 Morsel (3)

25 Final Greek letter (5)

26 Love intensely (5)

27 Day in spring on which the Resurrection is celebrated (6,6)

Down

2 Seeped (5)

3 Evergreen conifer (7)

4 Device that attracts iron (6)

5 Endure (5)

6 Assign a duty to (7)

7 Fine net used for veils (5)

8 Country, capital Moscow (6)

15 Childhood disease caused by deficiency of vitamin D (7)

17 Decline to vote (7)

18 Avenue (6)

19 Rubble, dust (6)

20 Male bee (5)

21 Plant also known as the century plant (5)

23 Alto violin (5)

68

Across

1 Person employed to carry luggage (6)

4 Battle (6)

7 Have to (4)

8 Diminished in strength or quality (8)

10 Vegetable, also known as squash (6)

12 Naturally illuminated (6)

14 Insusceptible (6)

17 Second in command (6)

19 Characterised by charm and generosity of spirit (8)

21 Old-fashioned form of the word 'you' (4)

22 Sheds hair or feathers (6)

23 Exclamation of joy or victory (6)

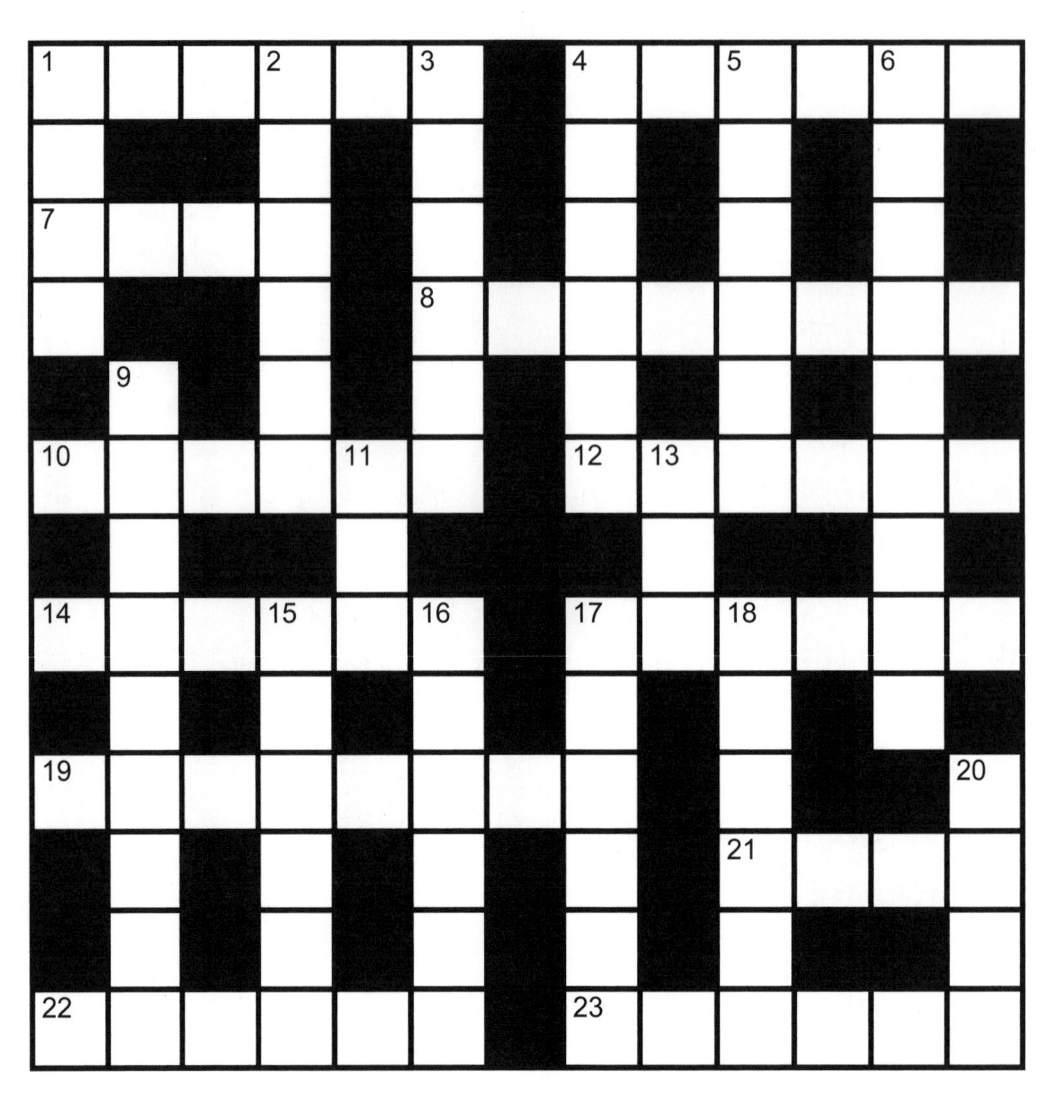

Down

1 Mountain lion (4)

2 Leash (6)

3 Critical evaluation (6)

4 Underground burial chambers (6)

5 Speak unfavourably about (6)

6 Provide physical relief, as from pain (9)

9 Oldest independent country in Europe (3,6)

11 Have (3)

13 Put into service (3)

15 Straighten (6)

16 Second book of the Old Testament (6)

17 Make downhearted (6)

18 Repressed (4-2)

20 French for 'father' (4)

69

Across

1 Nuclear (6)
7 Engage in boisterous, drunken merrymaking (7)
8 Television receiver (6)
9 Make believe (7)
10 Annul (6)
13 Become liable to (5)
15 Social insects (4)
16 Gen (abbr) (4)
17 Lofty proud gait (5)
18 Stings (6)
21 Suffocate, stifle (7)
23 Accumulate (6)
24 Agile performer (7)
25 Upward slope in the centre of a road (6)

Down

2 Eighth letter of the Greek alphabet (5)
3 Extremely angry (5)
4 Travelling show (4)
5 Republic in Central America (5,4)
6 Having branches or flower heads that droop (9)
10 Skilled artisan (9)
11 Stoppage (9)
12 Prevaricator (4)
14 Feline animals (4)
19 Coffee-chocolate drink (5)
20 Brownish-grey colour (5)
22 Biblical twin of Jacob (4)

70

Across

1 Note in music equal to half a minim (8)
5 Support for sails (4)
8 Nimble, spry (5)
9 Speak with others about (7)
10 Scholarly life (7)
12 Perceive words incorrectly (7)
14 Not in good condition (7)
16 Those who are older or higher in status (7)
18 Shine wetly (7)
19 Hearty enjoyment (5)
20 Ejected saliva from the mouth (4)
21 Constantly reading (8)

Down

1 Crack in a lip caused usually by cold (4)
2 Inflammation of the ear (6)
3 Gradual increase in volume (9)
4 Make attractive or lovable (6)
6 Lucky charm (6)
7 Organ on the surface of the tongue (5,3)
11 Natural and unavoidable catastrophes (4,2,3)
12 Methane produced when vegetation decomposes in water (5,3)
13 Heart condition marked by chest pain (6)
14 System of newsgroups on the internet (6)
15 Agency promoting teaching and the arts (inits) (6)
17 Spinning toys (4)

71

Across

1 Outerwear items (5)

5 Unwell (4)

7 State resembling deep sleep (6)

8 Greek letter (5)

9 Trio (9)

10 Large cask for beer or wine (3)

11 Holder (9)

15 Criminal who smashes a shop window with a vehicle (3-6)

19 Hour at which something is due (inits) (3)

20 Responses (9)

21 Delayed, postponed (2,3)

22 Guide (6)

23 Artificial (4)

24 Assignation between lovers (5)

Down

1 Talkative (6)

2 Add on, supplement (6)

3 Motionless (6)

4 Make nervous (8)

5 Start out on a sea voyage (3,4)

6 Smokestack (7)

12 Master copy (8)

13 Atlantic island, capital Funchal (7)

14 Flow thinly (7)

16 Holiday town (6)

17 Truth (6)

18 Most uncommon (6)

72

Across

1 Rise upward into the air (4)

3 Drug that produces numbness or stupor (8)

9 Device on an aircraft that controls lateral motion (7)

10 Flexible twig of a willow (5)

11 Fire-raising (5)

12 Fortress, stronghold (6)

14 Shun (6)

16 Man's item of formal dress (3,3)

18 Vocation (6)

19 Lowest point (5)

22 Conscious of (5)

23 Abandon (7)

24 Unpredictably excitable (8)

25 Have the courage (4)

Down

1 Brine (8)

2 Book of maps (5)

4 Medicinal plant (6)

5 Long race run over open terrain (5-7)

6 One of three children born at the same time (7)

7 Automobiles (4)

8 Son who rules during the absence or incapacity of a sovereign (6,6)

13 Stay of execution (8)

15 Indian bread (7)

17 Skilled trades (6)

20 Roman goddess of the hunt (5)

21 Tight-fitting hats (4)

73

Across

1 Most inflexible (8)

5 Contains the flow of (usually water) (4)

8 Irregular (8)

10 Framework that supports climbing plants (7)

11 Person who is tricked or swindled (6)

13 Draught animal (9)

15 Be larger in quantity (9)

18 Annul by rescinding (6)

19 Small axe with a short handle (7)

22 Port city on south-eastern Honshu, Japan (8)

23 Import tax (4)

24 State of inactivity (8)

Down

1 Deprive of food (6)

2 Blameless (8)

3 Acid associated with ants (6)

4 Exchange (4)

6 Four-wheeled motor vehicle (4)

7 Consolation (6)

9 Animal skin (7)

12 Sweet Madeira wine (7)

14 Turncoat (8)

15 In abeyance (2,4)

16 Take away (6)

17 Shows malicious satisfaction (6)

20 Diplomacy (4)

21 Semi-aquatic creature (4)

74

Across

1 Cheerfully irresponsible (5-2-5)

9 Exclamation of surprise (5)

10 Text of a song (5)

11 Turf (3)

12 Subdivision of an act of a play (5)

13 Charm (7)

14 Sullen (6)

16 Tortilla chips (6)

20 ___ Chapel, famous building containing a ceiling painted by Michelangelo (7)

22 Watery fluid of the blood (5)

24 Romanian monetary unit (3)

25 Mexican comrade (5)

26 Of the kidneys (5)

27 Not attached to or supported by anything (4-8)

Down

2 Joint in the leg (5)

3 Have (7)

4 Mature male goose (6)

5 Bush with fragrant flowers (5)

6 Building for cleaning vehicles (3,4)

7 Racing vessel (5)

8 Mineral used to make plaster (6)

15 Breathe (7)

17 Certain of (7)

18 Comparative figure of speech (6)

19 Sturgeon which is a valuable source of caviare (6)

20 Rod carried as a symbol (5)

21 Presses clothes (5)

23 Angry dispute (3-2)

75

Across

1 Unhealthy looking (6)
7 Relating to rural matters (8)
8 Do as you are told (6)
10 Swung back and forth (6)
11 Ballroom dance (5)
13 Encrusted with sugar (7)
16 Earthenware (7)
17 Natives of Geneva, for example (5)
20 Dried grape (6)
22 Beads used in prayer (6)
24 Earnings distributed to shareholders (8)
25 Looking at (6)

Down

1 Frozen fruit-flavoured dessert (6)
2 Narrow thin strip of wood (4)
3 Commonest liquid (5)
4 Glassware made of quartz (7)
5 Waste product useful as a fertiliser (4)
6 Marked by lack of attention (8)
9 Acute insecurity (5)
12 Having a strong distinctive fragrance (8)
14 Rolling treeless highland (5)
15 Bestowed upon (7)
18 Expressing in words (6)
19 Person excessively concerned about propriety and decorum (5)
21 Set of garments (usually of a jacket and trousers) (4)
23 Not in favour of (4)

76

Across

1 Roman slave who led an uprising against Roman legions (9)
8 Cetacean mammal (5)
9 Chap (3)
10 Unglazed leather (5)
11 Choral work (5)
12 Unrelaxed, taut (5)
13 Walk with long steps (6)
14 Trousers for casual wear (6)
18 Concentrate (5)
21 Troublesome children (5)
23 Unit of weight equivalent to 1000 kilograms (5)
24 Dressmaking aid (3)
25 Professional cooks (5)
26 Agriculture, farming (9)

Down

1 Capital of Oregon, USA (5)
2 Accounts checker (7)
3 Contorted (7)
4 Equipment for taking pictures (6)
5 Endearing (5)
6 Breakfast rasher (5)
7 Dam-building semiaquatic rodents (7)
13 Be enough (7)
15 Blue-flowered trailing plant (7)
16 Applauded (7)
17 City on the French Riviera, the site of an annual film festival (6)
19 Show submission or fear (5)
20 Save up for future use (5)
22 Cher's former singing partner (5)

77

Across

1 Countrified (6)
5 Scallywag (6)
8 Pimple (4)
9 Cultured (8)
10 General line of orientation (5)
11 Of a class (7)
14 Fragrant oily resin used in perfumes (6)
15 Manger (6)
17 Young hare (7)
19 Demon (5)
21 Lotion used in the treatment of sunburn (8)
23 Graphic symbol (4)
24 Squirm, wriggle (6)
25 Stickler (6)

Down

2 Relating to capital letters (5,4)
3 Lockjaw (7)
4 Masticate (4)
5 Gambling game with a revolving wheel and a small ball (8)
6 Condition (5)
7 Reverential salutation (3)
12 Characterised by an inability to mask one's feelings (9)
13 Person of subnormal intelligence (8)
16 Sir Laurence ___, English actor (1907–89) (7)
18 Raise to a higher rank or position (5)
20 Large brown seaweed (4)
22 Atmosphere (3)

78

Across

1 Pardoned (7)
5 Rise to one's feet (5)
8 Meeting arranged in advance (11)
9 Flashlight (5)
11 Motors (7)
13 Sighed with tiredness (6)
14 In or of the month preceding the present one (6)
17 Expand by lengthening or widening (7)
18 Confess (3,2)
19 Conduct an inquiry (11)
22 Numeral (5)
23 Grades, stages (7)

Down

1 Precisely (7)
2 Sporting trophy (3)
3 Most lacking in significance (9)
4 Responsibilities (6)
5 That girl (3)
6 Power of mental concentration (9)
7 Percussion instruments (5)
10 Providing personal satisfaction (9)
12 Of a horse, running at a fast pace (9)
15 Greek mythological musician, the husband of Eurydice (7)
16 Ran after (6)
17 Used a needle and thread (5)
20 Animal doctor (3)
21 Grow older (3)

79

Across

1 Large mass of frozen water (7)
6 Gossip (3)
8 Small pendant fleshy lobe at the back of the soft palate (5)
9 Adrift (7)
10 Perspiration (5)
11 Impoverished (8)
13 Seal of approval (6)
15 Emergence (6)
18 Woman who dances in a chorus line (8)
19 Plant grown as a lawn (5)
21 Foolish (7)
22 Hoaxes (5)
23 Definite article (3)
24 Cared for (7)

Down

2 Fabulous monster (7)
3 Type of cosmetic (8)
4 Piece of material inset to enlarge a garment (6)
5 Hard fruits (4)
6 Graceful antelope of Africa and Asia (7)
7 Hard-cased, winged creatures (7)
12 Albumen (3,5)
13 Become obstructed (7)
14 Wash (7)
16 Small fish (7)
17 Jesus (6)
20 Cleansing agent (4)

80

Across

1 Chronological records (6)

4 Plausible glib talk (6)

7 Japanese island (6)

8 Separate and distinct (8)

12 Overnight case (6)

14 Soft and mild (6)

15 Antonin ___, Czech composer (1841–1904) (6)

16 Orison (6)

18 Strong black coffee (8)

22 Look around a shop casually and randomly (6)

23 Counter-balance (6)

24 Clothing (6)

Down

1 Dull pain (4)

2 Italian town, birthplace of St Francis (6)

3 Blur (6)

4 Domestic swine (4)

5 Eye secretion (4)

6 Strong line (4)

9 Dispel gloom (5)

10 Farm implement used to break up soil (6)

11 Cuts into two equal pieces (6)

13 Dais (5)

16 Anxiety disorder (6)

17 Louisa May ___, author of Little Women (6)

18 Major monetary unit (4)

19 Steals (4)

20 Smut from a fire (4)

21 In this place (4)

81

Across

1 Submersible warships usually armed with torpedoes (1-5)

5 Assemble (3,2)

9 Record-keeper (9)

10 Board game (5)

11 Very steep cliff (9)

13 In next to first place (6)

15 Exclamation used to express surprise (2,4)

19 Commercially produced for immediate use (5-4)

21 Wanders about (5)

22 Outer layer of the skin (9)

24 Denigrate, defile (5)

25 Not faint or feeble (6)

Down

2 Framework of a railway carriage (5)

3 Equine animal (3)

4 Seedy (6)

5 Witchcraft (7)

6 Photocopier ink (5)

7 Announcement distributed to the media (5,7)

8 Ridiculous (12)

12 Make the sound of a dove (3)

14 Child's room (7)

16 Condiment made of fruit and sugar (3)

17 Sleeping compartments on a ship (6)

18 Maritime (5)

20 Capital of Jordan (5)

23 Sin (3)

82

Across

1 Outcome (6)

5 Leave, depart (3,3)

8 Pros and ___ (4)

9 Scholar (8)

10 Poison of snakes, etc (5)

11 Greatest in volume (7)

14 Bird which lays eggs in other birds' nests (6)

15 Marked by friendly companionship with others (6)

17 Apprentice (7)

19 Widely known and esteemed (5)

21 Edge of a highway (8)

23 Carpentry pin (4)

24 Nerve cell (6)

25 Missile discharged from a firearm (6)

Down

2 Institute legal proceedings against (9)

3 Cushion for kneeling on (as when praying in church) (7)

4 Group of people working together (4)

5 Marine creature (8)

6 Tendency (5)

7 Mr Geller, spoon-bender (3)

12 Drink, a mixture of lager and cider (9)

13 State of sticking together (8)

16 Strait (7)

18 Detection and location device (5)

20 Shed tears (4)

22 Poem intended or adapted to be sung (3)

83

Across

1 Clothes closet (8)
5 Disencumbers (4)
7 Experienced, competent (7)
8 Cause to jump with fear (7)
9 Entertainment venue (7)
11 Ancient rolled document (6)
14 Elbow-room (6)
16 Ample, plentiful (7)
18 Covered against loss (7)
21 Reaches a destination (7)
22 Way out (4)
23 Stout club (8)

Down

1 Sufferings, troubles (4)
2 Fix up (6)
3 Overwhelming defeat (4)
4 Plague, annoy continually (5)
5 Worthy of trust (8)
6 All at once (8)
10 Frozen rain (4)
11 Fortification fenced with a line of stout posts (8)
12 One who hopes for the best (8)
13 Stead (4)
15 Trill (6)
17 Fibre used for making rope (5)
19 Moved very fast (4)
20 Duck's feathers (4)

84

Across

1 ___ XVI, pope who resigned in 2013 (8)

5 Information reported in the papers (4)

7 Soothing ointment (7)

8 Feverish (7)

9 Milk pudding ingredient (7)

11 ___-Herzegovina, European country (6)

14 Thawed (6)

16 Plunder (7)

18 Word of transposed letters (7)

21 Disc used in various board games (7)

22 Free from danger (4)

23 Scolding old woman (8)

Down

1 Meat from cattle (4)

2 Dark grey cloud (6)

3 Type of food shop (abbr) (4)

4 Bottle that holds oil or vinegar for the table (5)

5 Maritime (8)

6 Located (8)

10 Gentle utterance used to call someone's attention (4)

11 Buildings used to house military personnel (8)

12 Having no intelligible meaning (8)

13 ___ Baldwin, former husband of Kim Basinger (4)

15 Fibre (6)

17 Destiny, fate (5)

19 Slightly open (4)

20 Major (4)

85

Across

1 Person who lights one cigarette immediately after another (5-6)

7 None in particular (3)

8 Genre of music originating in the 1950s (4,1,4)

9 Softly bright or radiant (7)

11 Contempt (5)

14 Harm, impair (6)

15 Remove by cutting out (6)

16 Pulverise (5)

19 Relating to glands near to the kidneys (7)

21 Miser (coll) (9)

23 Travel across snow (3)

24 City served by Jorge Newbery airport (6,5)

Down

1 Christmas song (5)

2 Variety (3)

3 More alien (8)

4 Puts to death (5)

5 Medium for communication (5)

6 Medical instrument used to inject (7)

10 Boasts (5)

12 Hidden supply (5)

13 Blind alleys (4,4)

14 Abominate (7)

17 Perform without preparation (2-3)

18 Hermann ___, novelist and poet (1877–1962) (5)

20 Thin strips of wood, used in plastering, etc (5)

22 Garland of flowers (3)

86

Across

1 Killing as an offering to a deity (11)

7 Burn slowly and without a flame (8)

8 Close by (4)

9 Marked by excessive self-indulgence (6)

11 End product (6)

13 Natives of Copenhagen, for example (5)

14 Military chaplain (5)

17 Alleviation (6)

20 Item which prevents a ship from moving (6)

22 ___ Blyton, author (4)

23 Final (8)

24 Manner of functioning (11)

Down

1 Arrangement (6)

2 Blusher (5)

3 Moves restlessly (7)

4 Consignment (5)

5 Piece of music for nine instruments (5)

6 Buccaneer (6)

10 Threshing instrument (5)

12 Covered entrance to a building (5)

14 Adhesive tape used in dressing wounds (7)

15 Without obligation (6)

16 Country associated with the meat dish souvlaki (6)

18 Pop music not issued by a major record company (5)

19 Light downy material (5)

21 Punctuation mark (5)

87

Across

1 Rarely found (6)
3 Tree with sharp thorns (6)
7 Having unattractive thinness, weedy (11)
10 Meant (8)
11 Had existence (4)
13 Amy Winehouse hit of 2007 (5)
14 Sweet made of flavoured sugar (5)
18 Army division (4)
19 Government levy (8)
21 Man to whom one is related by marriage (6-2-3)
22 Containing salt (6)
23 Loveliness (6)

Down

1 Well-built (6)
2 Knitted jacket (8)
4 Container for a bird (4)
5 Consented (6)
6 Woman whose face was said to have launched a thousand ships, ___ of Troy (5)
8 Doubt about the truth of something (9)
9 Exercise device consisting of an endless belt (9)
12 Periodic paperback publication (8)
15 Commits to a grave (6)
16 Place of safety or sanctuary (5)
17 Moving in a single direction (3-3)
20 Knock senseless (4)

88

Across

1 Lacking in quantity (6)

4 Baby's bed (6)

7 Exist in large quantities (6)

9 Vision (8)

11 Excavates (4)

14 Outstanding musician (7)

15 Woodworking tool (4)

16 Hollywood actress, Cameron ___ (4)

17 Movement of the sea in the same direction as the wind (3,4)

18 Tube of a tobacco pipe (4)

21 Reply of denial (8)

22 Fixed portion that is allotted (6)

24 Lessens in intensity (6)

25 Calm, with no emotional agitation (6)

Down

1 Burn with steam (5)

2 In the centre of (5)

3 Cardinal number (3)

4 Machine with a revolving drum used in making concrete (6,5)

5 Regions on diametrically opposite sides of the Earth (9)

6 Compass point (4)

8 Harmful to living things (11)

10 Respectful deference (6)

12 Cause to occur rapidly (6)

13 Sense something suspicious (slang) (5,1,3)

19 Two times (5)

20 Skin disease affecting domestic animals (5)

21 Star which ejects material (4)

23 Had a meal (3)

89

Across

4 Mental images occurring during sleep (6)

7 Person who is given the same appellation as another person (8)

8 Favouring one person or side over another (6)

9 Money extracted as a penalty (4)

10 Listening organ (3)

12 Religious doctrine (5)

13 Welfare (7)

16 Piece of cloth sewn under a zip or a pocket (7)

18 Explosion (5)

21 Appropriate (3)

22 Baby's bed (4)

23 Kitchen appliance, oven (6)

25 Alleviated (8)

26 Wild and rough (weather) (6)

Down

1 Salted roe of a sturgeon (6)

2 Forcefulness of expression (9)

3 Afterwards (5)

4 Question after a military operation (7)

5 Ms Braun, Hitler's mistress (3)

6 Breakfast food of untoasted dry cereals and fruits (6)

11 Voted back into office (2-7)

12 Artificial covering for a tooth (3)

14 Small insectivorous bird (3)

15 Wed again (7)

17 Detailed plan or design (6)

19 Eight-legged creature (6)

20 Reef of coral (5)

24 Mixture of white wine and cassis (3)

90

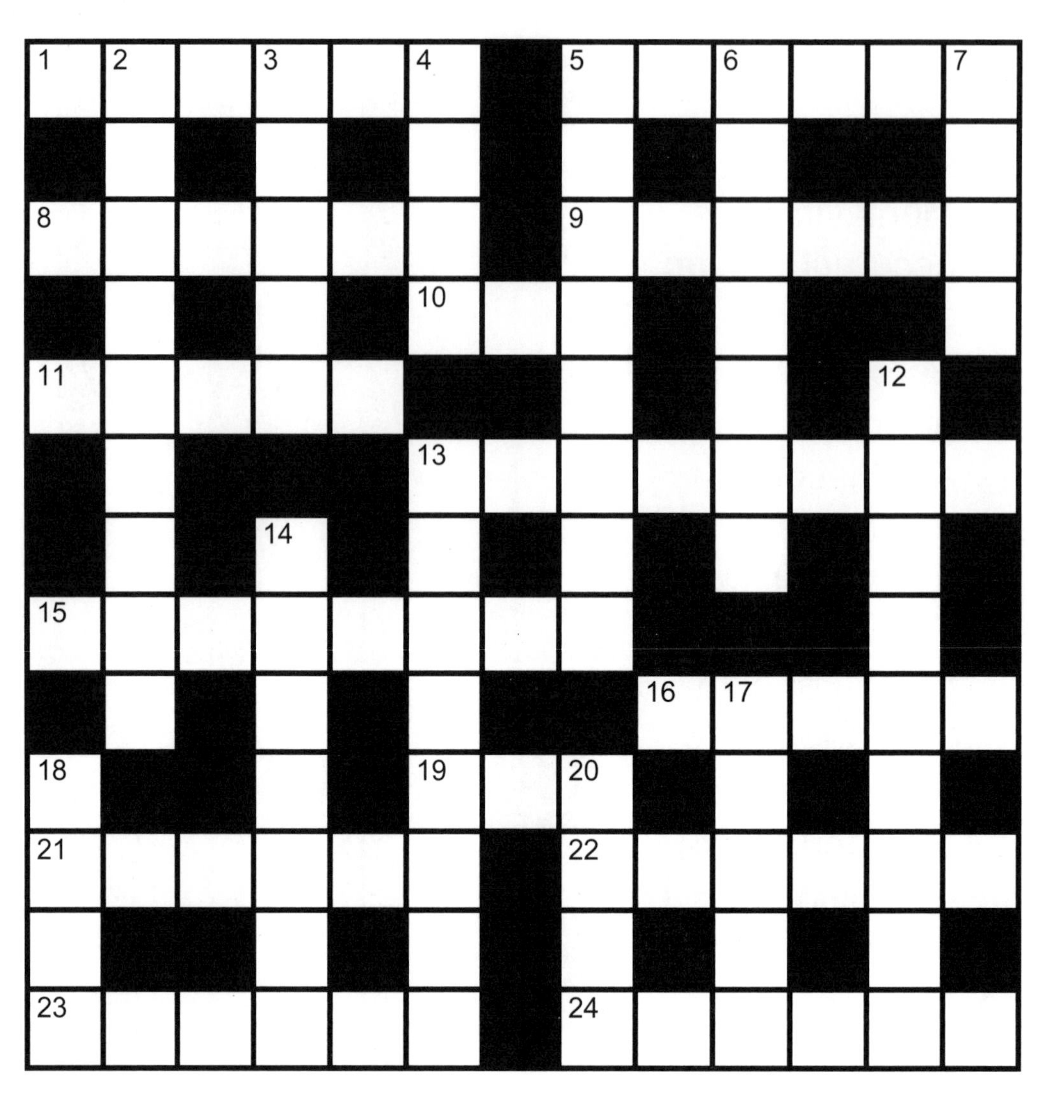

Across

1 Bodyguard (6)

5 National flag (6)

8 Sultanate in north-western Borneo (6)

9 Organisation of theatrical performers (6)

10 Form of address to a man (3)

11 Recipient of money (5)

13 Competition in which retailers cut purchase costs (5,3)

15 Unaffected by the passing years (8)

16 Capital of Afghanistan (5)

19 Fire's remains (3)

21 Basic unit of money in Hungary (6)

22 Slowly, in musical tempo (6)

23 Area, zone (6)

24 Bicycle for two riders (6)

Down

2 Expressing ridicule that wounds (9)

3 Snow leopard (5)

4 Word denoting a particular thing (4)

5 Internal organs, collectively (8)

6 Not as long (7)

7 Yuletide (4)

12 Manly (9)

13 Animal that lives by preying on others (8)

14 Jury's decision (7)

17 Anew (5)

18 Young newts (4)

20 Handle of a weapon or tool (4)

91

Across

1 Careless speed (5)

7 Skilled craftsman (7)

8 Resembling a dream (7)

9 Marked by uncontrolled excitement or emotion (7)

12 Difficult to understand, obscure (8)

14 Long detailed story (4)

16 Extremely wicked (4)

18 Squeezing together (8)

20 Native to the UK (7)

23 Obtain (7)

24 Visitors (7)

25 Appearing earlier in the same text (5)

Down

1 Waver (8)

2 Puts the ball into play (tennis) (6)

3 Viewed (4)

4 Fifty per cent (4)

5 Greek god of wine and fertility (8)

6 Disturbing the composure of (6)

10 Stank (6)

11 Noisy disturbance (6)

13 Improbable story (4,4)

15 Infringe on the rights of, in law (8)

17 Communicated in speech form (6)

19 Colour of the rainbow (6)

21 Chopped meat mixed with potatoes (4)

22 Shade of blue tinged with green (4)

92

Across

1 Remnant of the past (5)

4 Machine that plays selected records after a coin is inserted (7)

8 Vehicle from another world (inits) (3)

9 Characteristic (5)

10 Main artery of the body (5)

11 Attributed to (10)

13 Uses jointly (6)

15 Unnatural lack of colour in the skin (6)

18 Plant life in a particular region (10)

22 Slang term for ostentatious jewellery (5)

23 Targeted (5)

24 Cherry stone (3)

25 Shrill scream or cry (7)

26 Give qualities or abilities to (5)

Down

1 Without mercy (8)

2 Capital of Tibet (5)

3 Thin skin at the base of a fingernail (7)

4 Coupled (6)

5 Military fabric (5)

6 Object used in weightlifting (7)

7 Medical 'photograph' (1-3)

12 Fine translucent muslin, usually stiffened (8)

14 Artist's workroom (7)

16 Rouse, stir up (7)

17 Civil and religious leader of a Muslim state (6)

19 Tidal bore in a river (5)

20 Person with no fixed residence (5)

21 Flows back (4)

93

Across

1 Act of ascertaining an amount (11)

9 Female relatives (5)

10 Four-winged insect (3)

11 Form, category (5)

12 Cloudless (5)

13 Mathematics of shapes (8)

16 Plan for an activity or event (8)

18 Tertiary (5)

21 Celestial path (5)

22 Peculiar (3)

23 Grape-producing plants (5)

24 Calligraphy (11)

Down

2 Imaginary line around the Earth (7)

3 Shattered, broken into pieces (7)

4 Participant in a race (6)

5 Harmonious sounds (5)

6 Aristocrat (5)

7 Acknowledgment, identification (11)

8 Acted as a delegate (11)

14 Down payment (7)

15 Painful skin condition experienced in summer (7)

17 Nook (6)

19 Asian country (5)

20 Dropped steeply (5)

94

Across

4 Common farmyard bird (7)

7 Herb used in cooking (7)

8 Less good (5)

9 Bear fruit (5)

10 Edgar Allan ___, US writer and poet (3)

11 Brood (on) (5)

12 Taken unawares (9)

14 Analysis or study of meaning (9)

17 Garden buildings used for storage (5)

18 ___ de Cologne, perfume (3)

19 Passenger (5)

21 Egg-shaped object (5)

22 Equivalent word (7)

23 Restrain with fetters (7)

Down

1 Consistency (4)

2 Shooting star (6)

3 Facing or experiencing financial trouble or difficulty (4-7)

4 Main body (6)

5 Edible part of a nut (6)

6 Gratuitous (8)

8 Marital band worn on the finger (7,4)

12 Taking delight in beauty (8)

13 Felt hat with a creased crown (6)

15 Foam used in hair styling (6)

16 To set in from the margin (6)

20 Inclined surface (4)

95

Across

1 Lack of attention to one's own person (4-7)

7 State of being disregarded or forgotten (8)

8 Second letter of the Greek alphabet (4)

9 Starter course of a meal (6)

11 Cause to feel aggrieved (6)

14 Show off (5)

16 Occurring at regular intervals, seven times per week (5)

19 Pursued for food or sport (6)

22 Afternoon nap (6)

24 Large bodies of water (4)

25 Complex, full of twists (8)

26 Play of rainbow colours, as often seen on bubbles (11)

Down

1 Made small marks into the surface (6)

2 Mendicant monk (5)

3 Capable of being seen or noticed (7)

4 Relating to the moon (5)

5 Small house in the woods (5)

6 Make numb (6)

10 Prickle, barb (5)

12 ___ Khan (3)

13 Ovens used to fire pottery (5)

15 Her (3)

16 Arid regions of the world (7)

17 Selected (6)

18 Canine film star (6)

20 Weapon that delivers a temporarily paralysing electric shock (5)

21 Outmoded (5)

23 Derive, evoke (5)

96

Across

1 Level a charge against (6)
7 Injurious to health (7)
8 Consortium of companies formed to limit competition (6)
9 Cocktail made of gin or vodka with dry vermouth (7)
10 Assistant (6)
13 Hand tool for boring holes (5)
15 Deposits (4)
16 Thought (4)
17 Belonging to them (5)
18 Laundry appliance used for squeezing out water (6)
21 Move forward (7)
23 Wandering tribesmen (6)
24 Make free from confusion or ambiguity (4,3)
25 Small vicious animal employed in unearthing rabbits (6)

Down

2 Fad (5)
3 Military blockade (5)
4 Unconscious state (4)
5 Person who is an authority on past events (9)
6 Spying (9)
10 Act of mass destruction and loss of life (9)
11 As fast as possible (4-5)
12 Run competitively (4)
14 Microbe (4)
19 Roused from slumber (5)
20 Narrow shelf (5)
22 Hint (4)

97

Across

1 Rounded thickly curled hairdo (4)
3 Pleasure seeker (8)
7 Change from a gaseous to a liquid state (8)
8 German motor manufacturer (4)
9 Animal-drawn sledge (6)
10 Underhand (6)
11 Apprehension (5)
12 Hindu social class (5)
15 Characterised by romantic association (6)
18 Hairpiece (6)
19 Bundle of straw or hay (4)
20 Idle (8)
21 Timid, fearful (8)
22 Oxidisation caused by moisture in the air (4)

Down

1 Confront, solicit (6)
2 Attractively quaint, but not necessarily authentic (3-4)
3 Having the back and shoulders rounded (7)
4 Eats sparingly, in order to reduce weight (5)
5 Not a single person (2-3)
6 Dapple (7)
11 Series of pictures representing a continuous scene (7)
12 Short, curved sword (7)
13 Mechanical device on a camera (7)
14 Vast, sandy region (6)
16 Act of stealing (5)
17 Capital of Egypt (5)

98

Across

4 West Indian song (7)
8 River that flows through New York (5)
9 Spiny-finned fish (9)
10 Slowly, in music (5)
11 Dull, boring (9)
13 Plantation (6)
16 Herbivorous lizard of tropical America (6)
20 Mexican tortilla (9)
23 Indian corn (5)
24 Armistice, truce (9)
25 Daughter of a sibling (5)
26 Gamble, game of chance (7)

Down

1 Edible shellfish, a source of mother-of-pearl (7)
2 Unite (7)
3 U-shaped curve in a stream (5)
4 Marked by the appetites and passions of the body (6)
5 Jumping up (7)
6 Disney cartoon character (5)
7 Airport in Chicago (5)
12 Adult male person (3)
14 Earth's nearest star (3)
15 Ancient Greek or Roman warship (7)
17 Counselled (7)
18 Claimed, but not proved (7)
19 Sizeable hole (6)
20 Shine, surpass (5)
21 Recite with musical intonation (5)
22 Remedy (5)

99

Across

1 Drinking chocolate (5)

4 Ceremonial dinner party (7)

8 Animal disease (9)

9 Characteristic of a sheep (5)

10 Take back ownership (9)

13 Scented lozenge used to sweeten the breath (6)

14 Little crustacean (6)

16 Hard up (9)

19 Blood pump (5)

20 Sauce for pasta (9)

22 Spread open or apart (7)

23 Squeeze (5)

Down

1 Habitual, inveterate (7)

2 Mechanism for keeping an automobile at a set speed (6,7)

3 British snake (5)

4 Form of transport, double-decker (3)

5 Requires (5)

6 Impossible to foretell (13)

7 Changes direction (5)

11 Exactly matched (5)

12 Fertile desert areas (5)

15 Political organisations (7)

16 Bundles (5)

17 Elephant tusk substance (5)

18 Very penetrating and clear (5)

21 Also (3)

100

Across

1 Alarming, scary (5-8)

7 Expires (4)

8 Baby cat (6)

9 Portable shelters (usually of canvas) (5)

10 Item used to carry many cups at once (4)

12 Of the eyes (6)

13 Cooks in an oven (5)

15 Consumed (5)

18 Pencil mark remover (6)

20 Render unconscious (4)

21 Small terrestrial lizard (5)

22 Small ornamental case worn on a necklace (6)

23 Cattle shed (4)

24 Emission contributing to global warming (10,3)

Down

1 Tranquillise (6)

2 Malicious (5)

3 Tribes (5)

4 Annoying (7)

5 Capacity for rational thought (9)

6 Support for a travelling crane (6)

11 Slide of snow from a mountainside (9)

14 Cause friction, chafe (7)

16 Weariness after a flight (3-3)

17 Not if (6)

19 Slow-moving outlet of a lake (5)

20 Animal prized for its fur (5)

101

Across

1 Piece of open land for recreational use (4)

3 Ornament worn around the wrist (8)

9 Trip (7)

10 Audacity (5)

11 Clouded as with sediment (5)

12 Reins (7)

13 Barely noticeable (6)

15 Position of a person in society (6)

18 Trod (7)

19 Fails to win (5)

21 Played a part (5)

22 Concentrated (7)

23 Sections of text (8)

24 Requests (4)

Down

1 Night attire (7)

2 Ball-shaped (5)

4 Beat, as in music (6)

5 Express pleasure at someone's achievement (12)

6 Greatest in size (7)

7 Forest plants (5)

8 Reference work containing articles on various topics (12)

14 Gulps of air (7)

16 Methods (7)

17 Look up to (6)

18 Walk heavily (5)

20 Drops down (5)

102

Across

1 Tool used for bending wire (6)

4 Provided with shelter from the sun (6)

7 Lower limbs (4)

8 Inflicted with a virus (8)

10 Fabricate, make up (6)

12 Inferior substitute or imitation (6)

14 Playing card suit (6)

17 Grass producing an edible grain (6)

19 Severe recurring headache (8)

21 Sort, kind (4)

22 Dr ___, fictional character whose alter ego was Mr Hyde (6)

23 Morphine derivative (6)

Down

1 Inner surface of a hand (4)

2 Make certain (6)

3 Actor's lines (6)

4 Muffle, suppress (6)

5 Calculating machine (6)

6 Crucial (9)

9 Unable to be washed away or erased (9)

11 Egg of a louse (3)

13 Wheat-like cereal plant (3)

15 Something unusual – perhaps worthy of collecting (6)

16 Whine in a tearful manner (6)

17 Hold in a tight grasp (6)

18 Clergyman assisted by a curate (6)

20 Non-flowering plant (4)

103

Across

1 Pastry dishes (4)

3 Soft leather shoe (8)

9 Large structure for open-air sport (7)

10 Dark period (5)

11 Poorly thought out (3-9)

14 Beat hard (3)

16 Follow as a result (5)

17 Golfing device (3)

18 Piece of ornamented cloth that protects the back of a chair (12)

21 Frequently (5)

22 Hamlet (7)

23 US city famous for entertainment and gambling (3,5)

24 Precious stones (4)

Down

1 Capable of happening or existing (8)

2 Electronic message (5)

4 Electrical resistance unit (3)

5 Substantial, large in amount (12)

6 One of the parts into which something naturally divides (7)

7 Brief written record (4)

8 Failure to comply (12)

12 ___ del Sol, popular Spanish resort (5)

13 Intrepid (8)

15 Written account of a meeting (7)

19 Glide across ice (5)

20 Painful sore (4)

22 By way of (3)

104

Across

1 Authorisation to go somewhere (4)

3 Awesomely large (8)

9 Chemical used in reactions (7)

10 Deplete of resources (5)

11 Fragrant resin used as incense (5)

12 Product of coal tar extensively used in dyeing (7)

13 Official order (6)

15 Up until this time (6)

17 Maker (7)

18 Disreputable wanderer (5)

20 Insect in the stage between egg and pupa (5)

21 Made up of famous top performers (3-4)

22 Responding (8)

23 River of Russia and Kazakhstan (4)

Down

1 Vertical (13)

2 Remove unwanted hair (5)

4 Declare illegal (6)

5 Piece of folklore passed on by word of mouth (3,5,4)

6 Shore next to the coast (7)

7 Lowest rank of non-commissioned army officer (5,8)

8 Correctional institution (12)

14 Make free from confusion (5,2)

16 Consecrate (6)

19 Communion table (5)

105

Across

1 Bag made of hessian or plastic (4)

3 Rooted to the spot (8)

9 Draws out a reply or reaction (7)

10 Deep yellow colour (5)

11 Low-priced (5)

12 Systematic investigation of a matter of public interest (7)

13 Froth produced by soap (6)

15 Cleanses with soap and water (6)

18 More lustrous (7)

19 Excessive nasality in speech (5)

21 Pried (5)

22 Conjecture (7)

23 Till where money is taken for goods purchased (4,4)

24 Flesh used as food (4)

Down

1 Plate for making identical copies (7)

2 Censure severely (5)

4 Egyptian statesman who nationalised the Suez Canal (6)

5 Administrative centre of an enterprise (12)

6 Trash (7)

7 Unclean (5)

8 Lacking subtlety and insight (6-6)

14 Longs for a drink (7)

16 Drop a hint (7)

17 Goes up (6)

18 Of sound (5)

20 Burning (5)

106

Across

4 Cycle rickshaw (7)

8 French goodbye (5)

9 Obviate (9)

10 Group of warships (5)

11 Incite (9)

13 Not awake (6)

16 Mood (6)

20 Ritual killing (9)

23 Mood disorder (5)

24 Wooing (9)

25 Identifying appellation (5)

26 Field of study (7)

Down

1 Lustrous material (7)

2 Ore (7)

3 Civilian dress worn by a military person (5)

4 Local church community (6)

5 Feel distaste towards (7)

6 ___ Schumann, composer of piano music and wife of Robert Schumann (1819–96) (5)

7 Beautiful young woman (5)

12 Foot digit (3)

14 Bathing resort (3)

15 Long, formal letter (7)

17 Celestial bodies (7)

18 Connected (7)

19 Lightweight protective helmet (coll) (3,3)

20 Hosiery items (5)

21 Tiny morsel of bread (5)

22 Void of content (5)

107

Across

1 Assigned to a station (5)

5 Item of crockery (4)

7 Block the passage through (6)

8 Stalks of a plant (5)

9 Sure thing (9)

10 Large vase (3)

11 Something added to food to make it taste more sugary (9)

15 Ability to attract and charm people (9)

19 Reverence (3)

20 Foodstuffs and household supplies (9)

21 No longer new, uninteresting (5)

22 Association of sports teams (6)

23 Walking-stick (4)

24 Burdened (5)

Down

1 Rich soup made from shellfish (6)

2 Coils of worsted yarn (6)

3 Object thrown in athletic competitions (6)

4 Constantly in motion (8)

5 Wanted intensely (7)

6 Was in an agitated emotional state (7)

12 Navigable channel (8)

13 Capsicum spice (7)

14 Finger joint (7)

16 Black marine mollusc (6)

17 Rove in search of booty (6)

18 Belittle (6)

108

Across

1 Acid found in vinegar (6)
5 Bright in colour (6)
8 Loses brightness (4)
9 False (6)
10 Private instructor (5)
11 Female pantomime character (4)
12 Beers (4)
13 Be preoccupied with something (6)
15 One-hundredth of a dollar (4)
17 Recounted (4)
19 Begrudge (6)
20 Primitive, mainly aquatic organism (4)
21 Genre of popular music (4)
22 Informal term for money (5)
24 Harsh, stern (6)
25 Disease of the skin (4)
26 Military trainees (6)
27 Annoy persistently (6)

Down

2 Money (7)
3 Appreciation (5)
4 Insincere talk about religion or morals (4)
5 Number indicated by the Roman XIV (8)
6 Exist longer than (7)
7 Put on clothes (7)
14 Unwarranted, without foundation (8)
15 Creation of the highest excellence (7)
16 Acrobat's swing (7)
18 Aromatic or medicated tablet (7)
21 Close-fitting trousers of heavy denim (5)
23 Applaud (4)

109

Across

1 Highest female voice (7)
8 Military conflict (7)
9 Flight company (7)
10 Brainteaser (6)
12 Rough (6)
13 Australian musical instrument, played by holding in both hands and flexing (6,5)
17 Sympathetic compatibility (6)
20 Paper handkerchief (6)
23 Make a list of (7)
24 Lewd (7)
25 Draw back (7)

Down

1 Mariners (6)
2 Covered and often columned entrance to a building (7)
3 Generally accepted truth (5)
4 Due (4)
5 Well done! (5)
6 Manufacturer (5)
7 Person who carries equipment on an expedition (6)
11 Sickened, was ill (5)
12 Ancient unit of length (5)
14 Impatient, especially under restriction or delay (7)
15 Large terrestrial monkey, with a dog-like muzzle (6)
16 Feel contrition (6)
18 Green salad vegetable (5)
19 Jolly ___, pirates' flag (5)
21 Clumsy (5)
22 Coffin stand (4)

110

Across

1 Sequence of instructions a computer can interpret (7)

6 Fall guy (3)

8 Existing (5)

9 Aircraft pilot (7)

10 Skid (5)

11 Sheets and pillowcases (3,5)

13 Small pouch for shampoo, etc (6)

15 Entreaty (6)

18 Colourful explosive device (8)

19 Glacial (5)

21 Grinding food in the mouth (7)

22 Genetic copy (5)

23 Brandy measure (3)

24 Provided again with weapons (2-5)

Down

2 Coastal area between La Spezia in Italy and Cannes in France (7)

3 Kept, held back (8)

4 Wonder (6)

5 Soft fruits packed with seeds (4)

6 Act as a go-between (7)

7 Common, not specific (7)

12 Mayfly (8)

13 Anchorage (7)

14 Gather together (7)

16 Bring about (7)

17 Nipper at the end of a claw (6)

20 Protective covering of a building (4)

111

Across

1 Jangle (5)

7 Pastoral (7)

8 Natural height of a person (7)

9 Wine merchant (7)

12 Deliciously juicy (8)

14 Fall silent (4)

16 Movable organ for flying (4)

18 Leaving one's job due to age (8)

20 Imagination unrestricted by reality (7)

23 Original disciple (7)

24 Trash can (7)

25 ___ Island, New York Bay area (5)

Down

1 Proportion of revenue over outlay in a given period of time (4,4)

2 Fills with apprehension (6)

3 Surfeit (4)

4 Capital of Ukraine (4)

5 Manufacturer of bows and arrows (8)

6 Large streams (6)

10 Being in the original position (2,4)

11 Grieves (after a death) (6)

13 Consider carefully and deeply (8)

15 Royal title (8)

17 Greek character whose wings melted when he flew too close to the sun (6)

19 Enter drop by drop (6)

21 Sharp tug (4)

22 Bird symbolising peace (4)

112

Across

1 Popular Italian dessert (8)

5 Caution (4)

9 Fifth letter of the Greek alphabet (7)

10 Flip to a vertical position (2-3)

11 Think again! (10)

14 Assuaged (a thirst) (6)

15 Plaid associated with Scotland (6)

17 Flavour sensation that remains following eating or drinking (10)

20 Turns or places at an angle (5)

21 Nutty sweet (7)

22 Bird's construction (4)

23 Pennant (8)

Down

1 Makes a knot (4)

2 Hasty (4)

3 Shape consisting of four arrowheads with their points towards the centre (7,5)

4 Detection device (6)

6 Short account of an incident (8)

7 Lasting (8)

8 Demonstrate or verify by evidence (12)

12 Hired murderer (8)

13 Serving woman (8)

16 Floor covering (6)

18 Motion picture (4)

19 Successor (4)

113

Across

1 Struck violently, slammed (6)

8 Conceited and self-centred people (8)

9 Compulsory force or threat (6)

10 Music tape (8)

11 Natural spring which gives out steam (6)

12 Addition (8)

16 Characterised by lightness and insubstantiality (8)

18 Chase away (6)

21 Professor who is retired from assigned duties (8)

23 Choose not to participate (3,3)

24 Person who owns a guest-house (8)

25 Spookier (6)

Down

2 Entertain (5)

3 Conjecture (5)

4 Give an account of (8)

5 Sprockets (4)

6 Became broader (7)

7 Expresses in words (6)

11 Change course in sailing (4)

13 Blister near the mouth caused by a viral infection (herpes simplex) (4,4)

14 Latin phrase meaning 'and elsewhere' (2,2)

15 Having hair on the chin (7)

17 High-spirited romping girl (6)

19 Indian lute (5)

20 Ooze (5)

22 Lacking excess flesh (4)

114

Across

1 Acutely insightful and wise (7)

7 Transportation of goods by truck (7)

8 Flat mass of frozen water floating at sea (3,4)

10 Capable of meeting financial obligations (7)

11 Becomes bubbly, frothy (5)

12 Confidently aggressive (9)

16 In the act of committing a crime (3-6)

18 Condescend (5)

20 Jittery (7)

23 Country, capital Kiev (7)

24 Female ruler of many countries (7)

25 Utmost (7)

Down

1 Inhale audibly through the nose (5)

2 Got ready (8)

3 Dissertation (6)

4 Basic knitting stitch (4)

5 Front of the human head (4)

6 'Fab' 1960s group (7)

9 Capital of Zambia (6)

13 Steering mechanism at the stern of a vessel (6)

14 Able to recognise or draw fine distinctions (8)

15 Showing signs of having had too much alcohol (7)

17 Neglect (6)

19 Female relative (5)

21 Wholly absorbed as in thought (4)

22 Conform (4)

115

Across

1 Purloins (6)

5 South American rodent resembling a small beaver (5)

9 Pronounce clearly (9)

10 Founder of the Bolsheviks (5)

11 Fatigue (9)

13 Upright wooden posts used in cricket (6)

15 Visible suspension in the air (6)

19 Items often eaten roasted at Christmas time (9)

21 City and port on the coast of south-east Florida (5)

22 Flat paving slab (9)

24 Mixer drink (5)

25 Anything having existence (6)

Down

2 More genuine (5)

3 Joan of ___, French heroine (3)

4 Moved along a winding path (6)

5 Area of London (7)

6 Fine cords of twisted fibres (5)

7 Incurious (12)

8 Second half of the Christian Bible (3,9)

12 Deciduous tree (3)

14 World's largest ocean (7)

16 Humorous play on words (3)

17 Invalidate (6)

18 Elder brother of Moses (5)

20 Submersible warship, associated with WWII (1-4)

23 Posed for artistic purposes (3)

116

Across

1 Lacking in insight (6)

4 Prickly desert plant (6)

9 Attack by planes (3,4)

10 Green with growing things (7)

11 Employment (5)

12 Have in common (5)

14 Galas (5)

15 Small boat (5)

17 Rich cake (5)

18 Japanese warrior (7)

20 Fall to a lower level (7)

21 Swiss cottage (6)

22 Endured (6)

Down

1 Not clear (6)

2 Herb with leaves often used in vinegar (8)

3 Sophisticated, smooth (5)

5 Lecture (7)

6 Large, edible marine fish (4)

7 Sculpture (6)

8 Recklessness in politics or foreign affairs (11)

13 Scaremonger (8)

14 Cap which protects the tip of an umbrella (7)

15 Characteristic of the universe (6)

16 Rely (6)

17 Bone in the leg (5)

19 Aluminium silicate mineral (4)

117

Across

1 Turn into (6)

4 Rough area on the skin (6)

9 Novice, learner (7)

10 Portable light (7)

11 Stagger (5)

12 Flood, rush (5)

14 Ant (5)

15 Component parts of a skeleton (5)

17 Money risked on a gamble (5)

18 Perpetual (7)

20 Large imposing building (7)

21 Names of literary compositions (6)

22 Authoritative command (6)

Down

1 Armed fight (6)

2 President (8)

3 Division of the year (5)

5 In the middle of (7)

6 Delicate, woven and decorative fabric (4)

7 Primitive multicellular marine animal (6)

8 Voluntarily assumed or endured (4-7)

13 Scratchy (8)

14 Concentrated extract (7)

15 Bosom (6)

16 Fraudulence (6)

17 River which flows through Paris (5)

19 Small narrow pointed missile that is thrown (4)

118

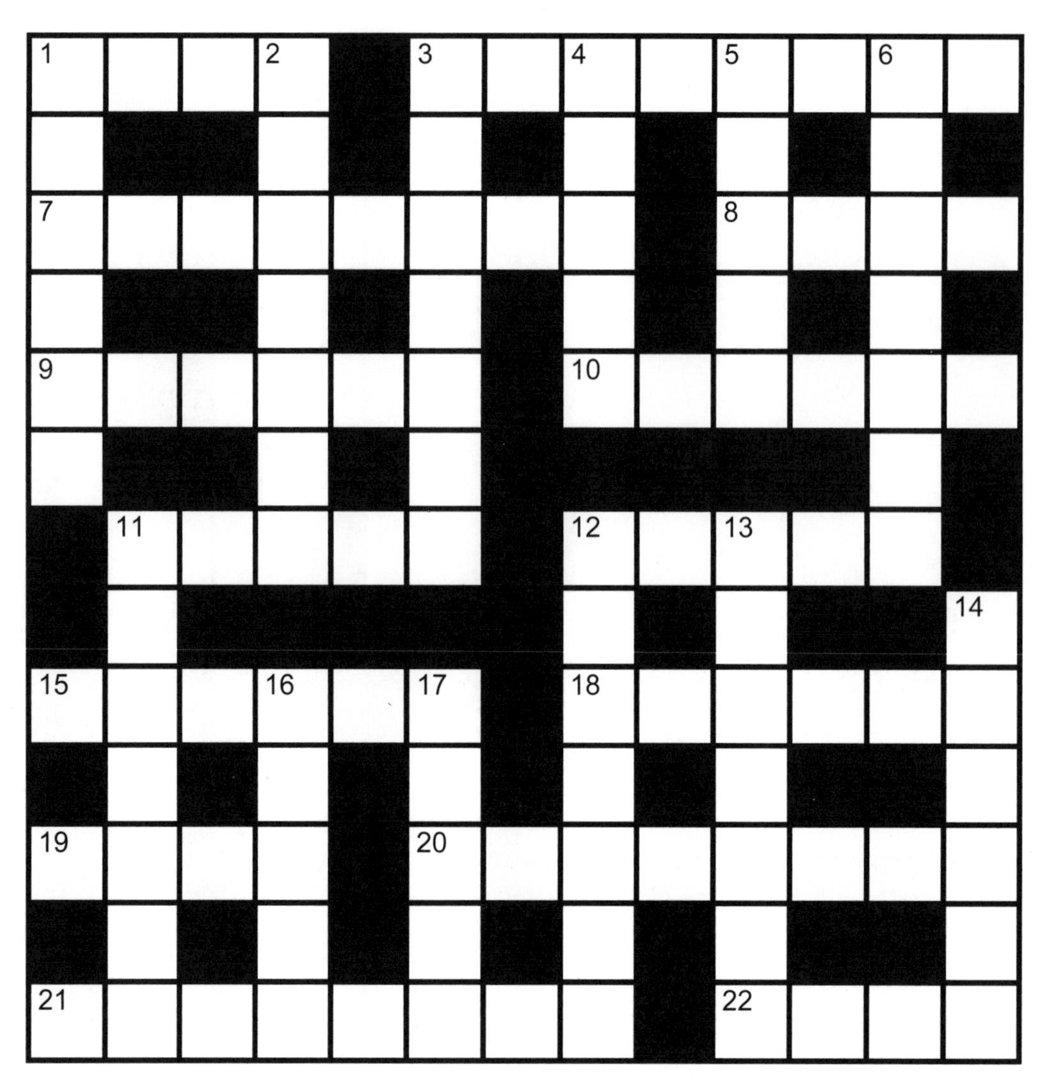

Across

1 Formal offers at an auction (4)

3 Motley assortment of things (8)

7 Individuality (8)

8 Pipe, conduit (4)

9 Sudden (6)

10 Part of a flower which holds the anther (6)

11 Cathedral priest (5)

12 Pungent (5)

15 Widely cultivated root vegetable (6)

18 Mick ___, English rock star associated with the Rolling Stones (6)

19 Central Hawaiian island (between Molokai and Kauai) (4)

20 Move in a wavy pattern (8)

21 Workable, possible (8)

22 Regulation (4)

Down

1 Nuptial (6)

2 Capital of Puerto Rico (3,4)

3 Make damp (7)

4 Painful eyelid swellings (5)

5 Means for communicating information (5)

6 Reach a desired goal (7)

11 Holy war (7)

12 Declare to be (7)

13 Occurring at fixed intervals (7)

14 Turn to ice (6)

16 Words used to refer to people, places or objects (5)

17 Measure the depth of something (5)

119

Across

1 Looking angrily distressed or distracted (4-4)

5 Young bears (4)

8 Gambling game using two dice (5)

9 Person who is not a Jew (7)

10 Merciful (7)

12 Brief break in a journey (4-3)

14 Motor vehicles specially modified to give high power and speed (3,4)

16 Tiredness (7)

18 Dodging, non-payment (7)

19 Ice house (5)

20 Long-necked bird (4)

21 Woven picture (8)

Down

1 Fuse (4)

2 Rough shelter at the side of a house (4-2)

3 Relaxed and informal in attitude or standards (4-5)

4 Flow over or cover completely (6)

6 Joined together (6)

7 Adds sugar, honey, etc (8)

11 Variety of peach (9)

12 Showing concern for the welfare of others first (8)

13 Several parallel layers of material (6)

14 Rupture in smooth muscle tissue (6)

15 Nocturnal wildcat of Central and South America (6)

17 Child's horse (4)

120

Across

1 Monarch's seat (6)

7 Practising abstention from alcohol (8)

8 Regretted (4)

10 Strip (6)

11 Glance over (4)

12 Unique (5)

13 Popular hot condiment (7)

17 Russian artificial satellite, the first to orbit the Earth (7)

19 Fowl (5)

21 Long walk usually for exercise or pleasure (4)

23 One who rides breaking waves (6)

25 Narrated (4)

26 Scenery intended to stand alone (3,5)

27 Elongated cluster of flowers (6)

Down

1 Either end of a bus route (8)

2 Marsh plant (4)

3 Gas formerly used as an anaesthetic (5)

4 Mythical being, half man and half horse (7)

5 Decoratively tied strips of ribbon (4)

6 Middle Eastern market (6)

9 Command with authority (6)

14 Saucepan stand (6)

15 Force out from a position (8)

16 Paper handkerchiefs (7)

18 Upset, offended (6)

20 Appliance that removes moisture (5)

22 Catch sight of (4)

24 English flower (4)

121

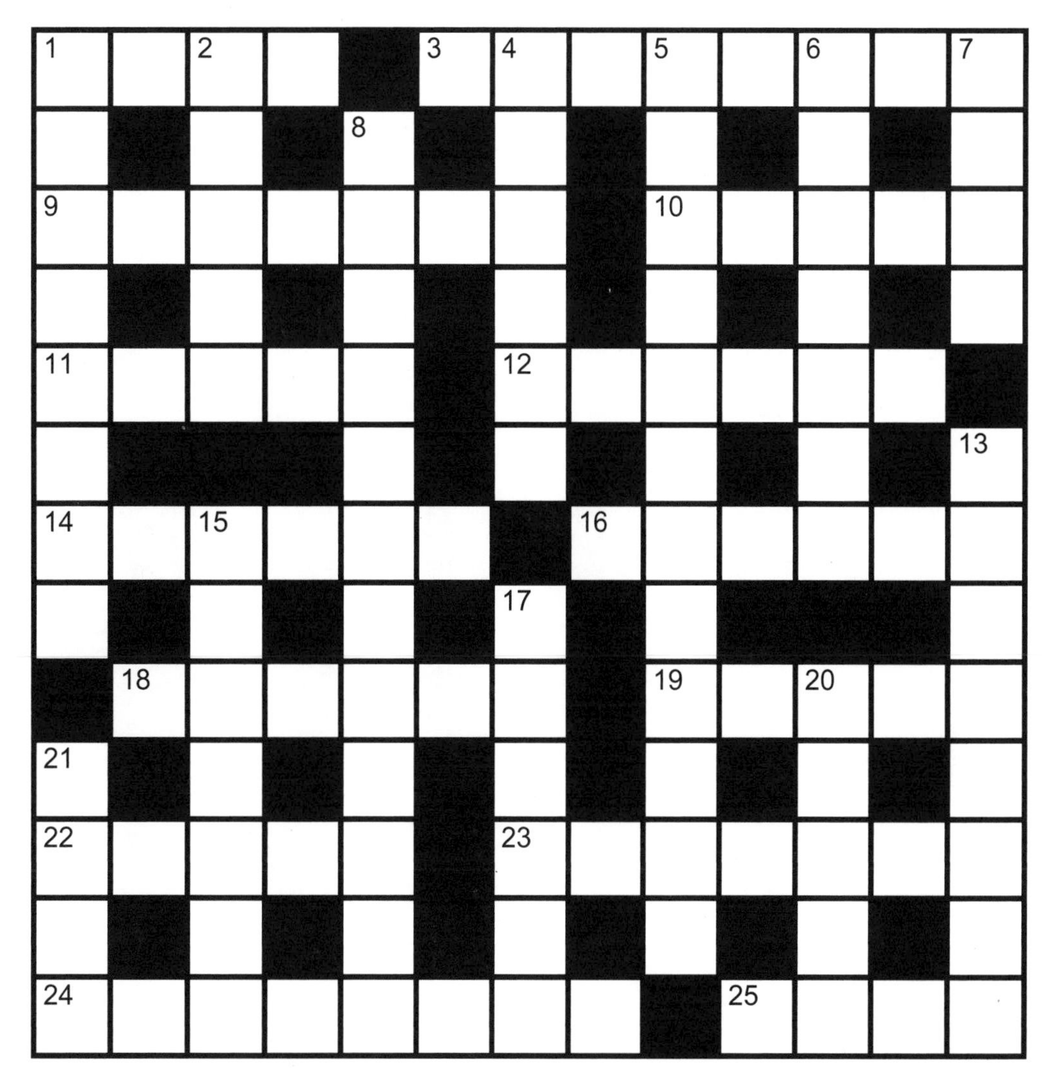

Across

1 Coffee shop (4)

3 Inhabitant (8)

9 Cooking utensil (7)

10 Product derived from cane or beet (5)

11 American raccoon (5)

12 Computer that provides access to shared resources (6)

14 Unfolded (6)

16 Utensil used to shred cheese, etc (6)

18 Small sofa (6)

19 Travels by boat (5)

22 Release, relinquish (3,2)

23 Having toothlike projections (7)

24 Location next to the warmest place in the house (8)

25 Thaw (4)

Down

1 Readily saleable foodstuff that is grown and gathered for the market (4,4)

2 Norse goddess (5)

4 Dead body (6)

5 Predictable, expected (12)

6 Increase (7)

7 Muslim of the former Ottoman empire (4)

8 Able to use both hands equally well (12)

13 Curved shape (8)

15 Citizen who has a legal right to vote (7)

17 Joined in matrimony (6)

20 Iconic mental representation (5)

21 Musical notation written on a stave (4)

122

1			2		3		4		5			6
7												
					8			9			10	
	11											
12				13			14					
15							16		17			
18			19		20							21
							22					
23							24					

Across

1 Musical composition written for six performers (6)
4 Involuntary vibration (6)
7 Attack another's territory (6)
8 Etch into a material or surface (8)
12 Deliberately causes a delay (6)
14 ___ Night, Christmas carol (6)
15 Great coolness and composure (6)
16 Objective (6)
18 Illegal action inciting resistance to lawful authority (8)
22 Phrase structure (6)
23 Protein which acts as a catalyst (6)
24 Held legally responsible (6)

Down

1 Large and hurried swallow (4)
2 Go on a journey (6)
3 Belonging to those people (6)
4 Tie-on labels (4)
5 Large container for liquids (4)
6 Actor's portrayal of someone (4)
9 High quality porcelain (5)
10 Hazard on a golf course (6)
11 Metal paper fastener (6)
13 Demarcation line (5)
16 Threads of metal foil (6)
17 African country of which Kigali is the capital (6)
18 Open skin infection (4)
19 Chancy (4)
20 Offshore territory (4)
21 Shaft on which a wheel rotates (4)

123

Across

1 Imbecile (7)

5 Ecstasy (5)

8 Ring or echo with sound (11)

9 Celtic language (5)

11 Item given to partly pay for a new one (5-2)

13 Shorn, tonsured (6)

14 Pierce with a sharp stake (6)

17 Deep red (7)

18 Locations (5)

19 Overwhelmed by wonder (3-8)

22 Purloin (5)

23 Remorse for conduct in the past (7)

Down

1 Vainglorious, extravagant or melodramatic conduct (7)

2 Bulgarian monetary unit (3)

3 Lacking in usefulness or value (9)

4 Formal agreement (6)

5 Long fluffy scarf (3)

6 Graceless (9)

7 Item of cutlery (5)

10 Lifeless (9)

12 Entrance fee (9)

15 Core, meaning (7)

16 Arch of the foot (6)

17 Popular game played with pieces of stiffened paper (5)

20 Long and slippery fish (3)

21 Range of knowledge (3)

124

Across

1 Carte ___, complete freedom to act as one wishes (7)

5 Ancient Mexican civilisation (5)

8 Shortening of a muscle (11)

9 Type of parrot (5)

11 Scrutinise (7)

13 Poem of fourteen 10- or 11-syllable lines (6)

14 Bowl-shaped vessels (6)

17 Colonist (7)

18 Special occasion (5)

19 Have room for (11)

22 Radio set (5)

23 In an abrupt manner (7)

Down

1 Turns into (7)

2 Beard found on a bract of grass (3)

3 Acrobatic movement using both hands and feet (9)

4 Greek mathematician nicknamed the 'Father of Geometry' (6)

5 ___ Baba (3)

6 Small orange (9)

7 Outer layer on bread (5)

10 Hold back (9)

12 Entrance used by performers and other theatre personnel (5,4)

15 Repletion (7)

16 On time (6)

17 Extract (metals) by heating (5)

20 Low-breed dog (3)

21 Expert (3)

125

Across

1 Exhibit aggressively (8)

5 Go round and round (4)

8 Web-footed turtle living in fresh or brackish water (8)

10 Unbearable physical pain (7)

11 Sound off (5)

12 One million periods per second (9)

15 Lawyers (9)

18 Onerous task (5)

19 Admiration (7)

22 Murder (8)

23 Sound reflection (4)

24 Showing profound esteem (8)

Down

1 Shirt fastener (6)

2 Having no weak points (8)

3 Crown or headband worn by a sovereign (6)

4 Short theatrical episode (4)

6 Funereal fire (4)

7 Stinging plant (6)

9 Someone legally empowered to witness signatures (6)

13 Harem guard (6)

14 Element used to purify water and as a bleaching agent (8)

15 Supply or impregnate with oxygen (6)

16 Copyist (6)

17 Smallest in number (6)

20 Utterance made by exhaling audibly (4)

21 Large and scholarly book (4)

126

Across

1 Very powerful (6)

3 Mended by sewing, as with socks, for example (6)

7 Grow worse (11)

10 One quarter or one third, for example (8)

11 Eyelid swelling (4)

13 Religious song (5)

14 Electronic device that generates a series of beeps (5)

18 "Beware the ___ of March", advice given to Julius Caesar (4)

19 More hairy, bushier (8)

21 Otherwise (11)

22 Red, globular salad vegetable (6)

23 Make up one's mind (6)

Down

1 Change, make different (6)

2 Strangle (8)

4 Gelling agent (4)

5 Stocking gauge measure (6)

6 Automaton (5)

8 Go beyond, surpass (9)

9 Person who holds radical views (9)

12 Death of part of the body (8)

15 Main meal of the day (6)

16 Part of the face below the eye (5)

17 Knitted or woven with a diamond-shaped pattern (6)

20 Vehicles from outer space (inits) (4)

127

Across

1 Protection (7)
5 Space created by the swing of a scythe (5)
7 Higher in position (5)
8 Itinerant Australian labourer (7)
9 Cultivating the land or raising stock (7)
10 Plant from which opium is obtained (5)
11 Make or become dimmer (6)
13 Malignant growth or tumour (6)
18 Form of theological rationalism (5)
20 Increased threefold (7)
21 Commissioned military officer (7)
22 Country, capital Accra (5)
23 Gains victory over (5)
24 Funeral procession (7)

Down

1 Completely filled (7)
2 Male ruler (7)
3 Rotary engine (7)
4 Leave a job voluntarily (6)
5 Fill quickly beyond capacity (5)
6 Crush by treading heavily (7)
12 Inflammable liquid widely used as an organic solvent (7)
14 Retaliator (7)
15 Picture made by sticking things together to form a montage (7)
16 Bureaucratic procedure (3,4)
17 Sloping print (6)
19 Subtraction sign (5)

128

Across

1 Moving or capable of moving readily (6)

7 Ray of light from Earth's satellite (8)

8 Bring under control (6)

10 Cashier (6)

11 Line on which music is written (5)

13 Gambling (7)

16 Railway building (7)

17 Word of greeting (5)

20 Hang on to (6)

22 Ant or beetle, for example (6)

24 Consignment (8)

25 Substance that turns red in acid (6)

Down

1 Fails to hit (6)

2 Tell tales (coll) (4)

3 Glowing fragment of wood or coal left from a fire (5)

4 Slogans, sayings (7)

5 Child of Adam and Eve (4)

6 Fatherly (8)

9 Piece of turf dug out of a lawn (5)

12 Worn to shreds (8)

14 Layers (5)

15 Person whose duty is to throw troublemakers out of a bar (7)

18 Physical science relating to light (6)

19 Tough sort of plastic (5)

21 Zealous (4)

23 Academic test (abbr) (4)

129

Across

4 Warning or proviso (6)

6 Bear in mind (8)

7 Blood vessel leading from the heart (6)

8 Clubs used in the game of cricket (4)

9 Pouch (3)

11 Commandeer (5)

12 Boldly resisting authority or an opposing force (7)

15 Amplifier (7)

17 Flexible joint (5)

20 Holy sister (3)

21 Harness strap (4)

22 Twisting force (6)

23 Colander (8)

24 Newborn children (6)

Down

1 Green parts that form the calyx of a flower (6)

2 Fast narrow current in the atmosphere or ocean (3,6)

3 Evil or corrupt practice (5)

4 Christmas banger (7)

5 Type of firearm (6)

10 Chinese gooseberry (4,5)

11 Raises (3)

13 Knotted item of clothing (3)

14 Novelty (7)

16 Asian temple (6)

18 Covering for the lower leg and ankle (6)

19 Breathe noisily during sleep (5)

130

Across

1 Inflammation of the stomach lining (9)

5 Circuit (3)

7 Adhered (6)

8 Commences (6)

10 Palm fruit (4)

11 Become alcohol (7)

13 Cut in three (7)

17 Delighted (7)

19 Requirement (4)

21 Ski race over a winding course (6)

22 Rectangular, dotted playing piece (6)

23 Side sheltered from the wind (3)

24 Game bird of the pheasant family (9)

Down

1 Taunt (4)

2 Light shoe with straps (6)

3 Graceful woodland animal (3,4)

4 Downright (5)

5 Dawdle (6)

6 Convinced (8)

9 In football, beyond a prescribed line or area (7)

12 Offer of marriage (8)

14 Line on a map connecting points of equal height (7)

15 Corrupt morally (6)

16 After (6)

18 Sailing vessel with a single mast (5)

20 Shower with love (4)

131

Across

1 Facade one presents to the world (7)
7 Manufactured, not occurring naturally (3-4)
8 Semi-precious yellow quartz (7)
10 Person with a record of failing (2-5)
12 Clean with a broom (5)
13 Relate (9)
17 Percussion instrument consisting of a pair of hollow pieces of wood (9)
20 Imbecile (5)
22 To a higher position (7)
25 Thankless wretch (7)
26 Everlasting (7)
27 Peninsula in Central America extending into the Gulf of Mexico (7)

Down

1 Rock-breaking tools (5)
2 Falls back, ebbs (8)
3 Rectifies (6)
4 One twelfth of a foot (4)
5 Musical instrument associated with Wales (4)
6 Small and pulpy edible fruits (7)
9 African antelope (6)
11 Judo belt (3)
14 Housing or outer covering (6)
15 Seeking advancement or recognition (8)
16 Brought a charge against (7)
18 Former US airline (1930–2001) (inits) (3)
19 Without effort (6)
21 Link up, connect (3,2)
23 Unwanted plant (4)
24 US city known for gambling casinos and easy divorce (4)

132

Across

1 Fortune-teller's globe (7,4)

9 Take part in a row (5)

10 Drink made by infusing dried leaves (3)

11 Dexterous (5)

12 Smudge, daub (5)

13 And so on (Latin) (2,6)

16 Distribute according to a plan (8)

18 Prods (5)

21 Fillip, incentive (5)

22 Hen's produce (3)

23 Book-length story (5)

24 Day of remembrance (11)

Down

2 Biblical wife of Isaac and mother of Jacob and Esau (7)

3 Act passed by a legislative body (7)

4 Fisherman (6)

5 Consecrate (5)

6 Espresso coffee with milk (5)

7 Person who earns a living by excavating burial places (5-6)

8 Stylist (11)

14 Walks with short unsteady steps (7)

15 Wash clothes (7)

17 Immature insects (6)

19 Inert gas (5)

20 Desert in north-eastern Egypt (5)

133

Across

1 Place where vehicles halt to discharge and take on passengers (3,4)

5 Section of an orchestra (5)

8 Rim (3)

9 Member of an irregular armed resistance force (9)

10 Deflect, fend off (5)

12 Fencing sword (4)

13 Ship's lounge (6)

15 Those people (4)

17 Sepulchre (4)

20 Superfluous, redundant (6)

22 Precipitate (4)

23 Influenced by corruption (3,2)

25 Highest mountain peak in the Alps (4,5)

26 Frost (3)

27 Linger (5)

28 Innumerable but many (7)

Down

1 Heavy material used to ensure stability (7)

2 Highest in excellence (7)

3 Garment worn on the lower half of the body (6)

4 Secret look (4)

6 Apparel (7)

7 Limbless reptile (5)

11 Deprivation (4)

14 Corrosive compound (4)

16 Keep under surveillance (7)

18 Survive longer than (7)

19 In the interval (7)

21 Breakfast food container (6)

22 Send (payment) (5)

24 Capital of Azerbaijan (4)

134

Across

1 Hypotheses (13)
7 Pouches (4)
8 Discord (6)
9 Musical compositions with words (5)
10 All right (4)
12 Cause to be indebted (6)
13 Region of South Africa, KwaZulu-___ (5)
15 Number indicated by the Roman LX (5)
18 Proverbs (6)
20 Russian emperor (4)
21 Covered with thin horny plates (5)
22 Minuscule (6)
23 Couple (4)
24 One who communicates by means of letters (13)

Down

1 Mechanical device that has a thrusting motion (6)
2 Impertinent (5)
3 Not sharp (5)
4 Lariats (7)
5 Brings about, launches (9)
6 Appeared (6)
11 White gypsum (9)
14 Diminishes (7)
16 Celtic language (6)
17 Fungus causing timber to crumble (3,3)
19 Oval fruit with a very large seed (5)
20 Keyed into a machine (5)

135

Across

1 Former French unit of currency (5)

4 Besotted (7)

7 Pale brown colour (5)

8 Part of the body (8)

9 Fatigued (5)

11 Pursuit of pleasure as a matter of ethical principle (8)

15 Revere (8)

17 Celtic priest (5)

19 Ornamental climbing plant (8)

20 Alternative (5)

21 Swift pirate ship (7)

22 Sticky plant extract (5)

Down

1 Untruth (9)

2 Oval-shaped edible nuts (7)

3 Shouting for (7)

4 Items of bed linen (6)

5 Protective covering on a boot or shoe (6)

6 Emblem representing power (5)

10 Measurable extent, eg height or breadth (9)

12 Jane ___, third wife of Henry VIII (7)

13 Administrative divisions of Switzerland (7)

14 Frogmen (6)

16 Finger-shaped cream cake (6)

18 Fashion reminiscent of the past (5)

136

Across

1 Shout, as if with joy or enthusiasm (5)

4 Arranged in close-packed rows (7)

8 Type of cobra (3)

9 Persuasive line of talk (5)

10 Regarding (5)

11 Maternity (10)

13 Chinese fruit having a thin brittle shell (6)

15 Breathe with a husky or whistling sound (6)

18 Criminal, outlaw (10)

22 Board used with a planchette (5)

23 Torpid (5)

24 British system of medical care (inits) (3)

25 Dentist's consulting room (7)

26 Horizontal part of a step (5)

Down

1 Capable of being cleansed in water without damage (8)

2 Hate coupled with disgust (5)

3 Artist's paint-mixing board (7)

4 Gaps (6)

5 Freshwater fish (5)

6 Ferrous mineral (4,3)

7 Very small circular shapes (4)

12 Left desolate or empty (8)

14 Keyboard instrument (7)

16 Register of victims to be eliminated (3,4)

17 Area in Germany around the upper Elbe river (6)

19 Rub out (5)

20 Fasten by passing rope through a hole (5)

21 Young men (4)

137

Across

1 Truthful (6)

7 Signal (usually a siren) that danger is over (3,5)

8 Bicycle accessory (4)

10 Woven shopping bag (6)

11 Grains on the beach (4)

12 Glossy, smooth (5)

13 Stately, refined (7)

17 Prevent from entering (4,3)

19 Causes acute discomfort (5)

21 Flip (a coin, for example) (4)

23 Boundary line (6)

25 Cobbler's stand (4)

26 Transducer used to detect and measure light (5,3)

27 Duty list (6)

Down

1 Mental state induced by suggestion (8)

2 Insensitive, dull to pain (4)

3 Slightly sticky to the touch (5)

4 In total (3,4)

5 Charitable gifts (4)

6 Large gun (6)

9 Document granting an inventor sole rights (6)

14 Rock fragments and pebbles (6)

15 Person who makes a will (8)

16 Flat-bottomed glass without a handle or stem (7)

18 Yippee! (6)

20 Utensil for cooking chips (5)

22 Sea-going vessel (4)

24 Harangue (4)

138

Across

1 Distress (5)

4 One who travels for pleasure (7)

7 Fastener with a threaded shank (5)

8 Hold back (8)

9 Compact mass, cluster (5)

11 Most brief (8)

15 Dashes a liquid against (8)

17 Place where milk, butter, cheese, etc is produced (5)

19 Talked indistinctly (8)

20 Emblem (5)

21 Knocked unconscious by a heavy blow (7)

22 Arab republic (5)

Down

1 Without clothing (9)

2 Meeting devoted to a particular activity (7)

3 Rotating gun enclosures (7)

4 Vehicles which run on tracks (6)

5 In an elaborate, generous or plentiful way (6)

6 Water at boiling temperature diffused in the air (5)

10 United States head of state (9)

12 Arrest (7)

13 Because of that (7)

14 Place where something begins (6)

16 Flowed in a spurt (6)

18 At a distance (5)

139

Across

1 Make-up used on the eyelashes (7)

5 Leaves out (5)

8 Tear apart (3)

9 Become one (9)

10 Embellish (5)

12 Deficient in beauty (4)

13 Swimming style (6)

15 Profound (4)

17 Small whirlpool (4)

20 Passes along (6)

22 Endorsement made in a passport (4)

23 Person afflicted with Hansen's disease (5)

25 Dispersed (9)

26 Female reproductive cells (3)

27 Cowboy contest (5)

28 Hand-thrown bomb (7)

Down

1 Imaginary sea nymph (7)

2 Expect, believe (7)

3 Arranges so as to be parallel or straight (6)

4 Gambling stake (4)

6 Large and often sumptuous tent (7)

7 Sleazy or shabby (5)

11 Warm and snug (4)

14 Combat between two mounted knights (4)

16 Childish talk (7)

18 Document certifying successful completion of a course (7)

19 Distance measured in three-foot units (7)

21 Vehicle for travelling on snow (6)

22 Peak of a cap (5)

24 Talk boastfully (4)

140

Across

1 Slow the growth or development of (6)

4 Sends a telegram (6)

7 US state, capital Richmond (8)

8 At another time (4)

9 Russian rulers (5)

10 Passage (7)

12 First day of the working week (6)

13 More neat (6)

15 Fund of money put by as a reserve (4,3)

18 Ejects with force (5)

20 Hindu princess (4)

21 Give up the throne (8)

22 Produce incisors, molars, etc (6)

23 Climb up (6)

Down

1 Direct one's attention on something (5)

2 Land, ground (7)

3 Bring back into original position (9)

4 Seat (5)

5 Connections (5)

6 US legislator (7)

11 Towards the centre of a sailing vessel (9)

12 Slender tower on a mosque (7)

14 Repeat (7)

16 Sound practical judgment (5)

17 Elegance and beauty of movement (5)

19 Rate of travel (5)

141

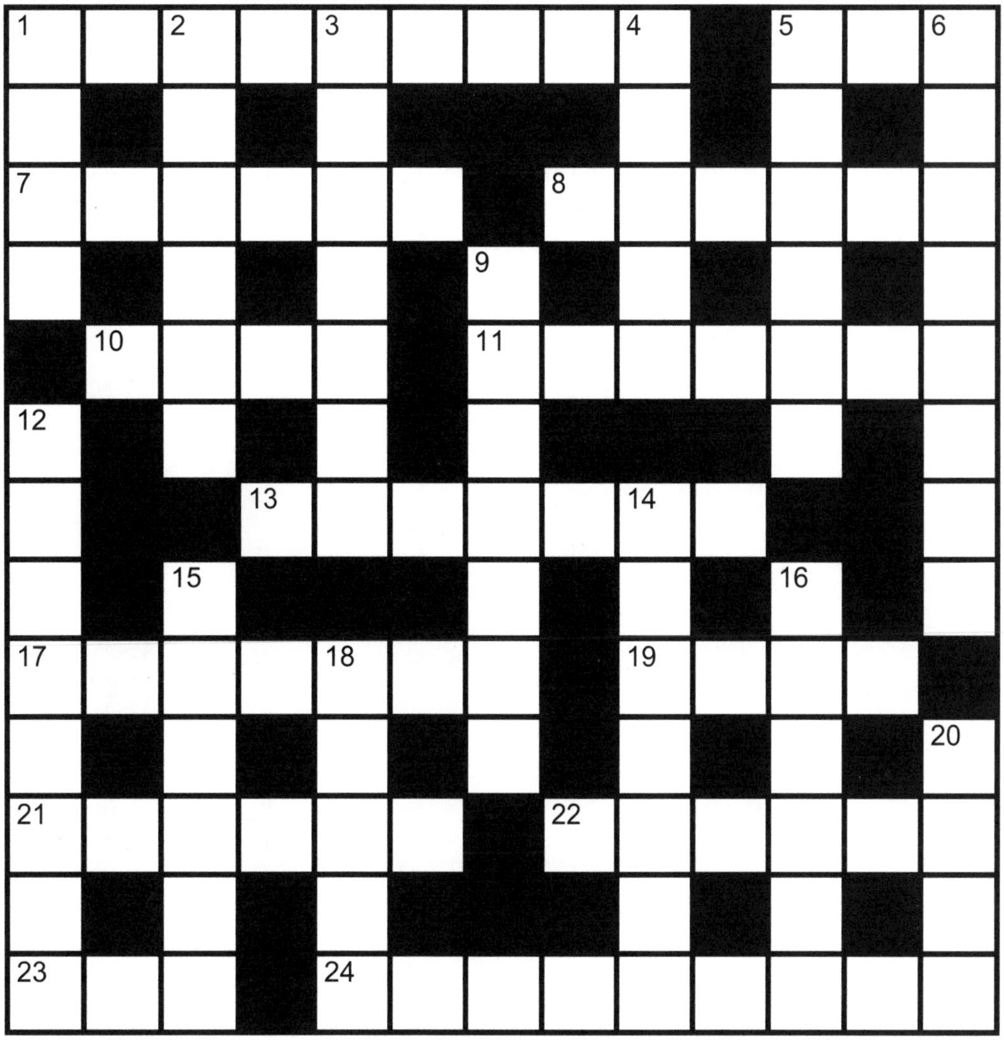

Across

1 Recovering readily from adversity (9)

5 Catch sight of (3)

7 Dignified and sombre in manner (6)

8 Tedious (6)

10 ___ Major, the Great Bear constellation (4)

11 Cut off the sun's light (7)

13 Mistake one thing for another (7)

17 Short preview of a film or TV programme (7)

19 Sudden short attack (4)

21 Pass from physical life (6)

22 Small informal restaurant (6)

23 Fruiting spike of a cereal plant (3)

24 Quickly aroused to anger (9)

Down

1 Dry biscuit, a teething aid (4)

2 Torrid (6)

3 Pain in the lower back (7)

4 Mythical cave-dwelling creature (5)

5 Containing little excess (6)

6 Keen or close watch (coll) (5,3)

9 Carry out an action (7)

12 Completely sane (coll) (3,5)

14 Continue to live, despite adversity (7)

15 Covered picnic basket (6)

16 Sieved (6)

18 Coniferous tree (5)

20 Crucifix (4)

142

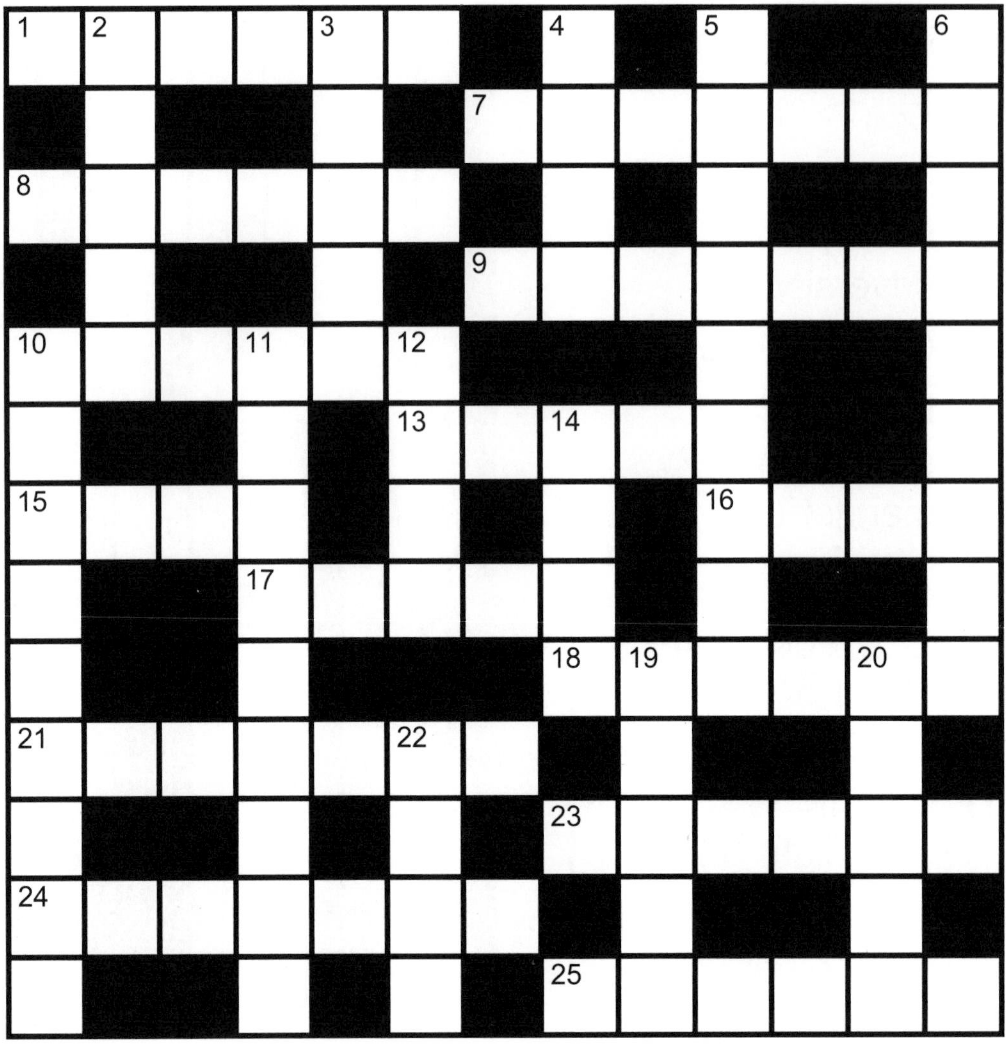

Across

1 Rook in the game of chess (6)

7 Threatening or foreshadowing evil (7)

8 Pass on, of information (6)

9 Organ of speech (7)

10 Plant with spiny bracts (6)

13 Annoyance (5)

15 ___ Karenina, novel by Leo Tolstoy (4)

16 At rest (4)

17 Welsh breed of dog (5)

18 Insect which rests with forelimbs raised as if in prayer (6)

21 Going by, overtaking (7)

23 One living temporarily in a tent (6)

24 Wither, especially due to loss of moisture (7)

25 In a mild, soft manner (6)

Down

2 Sprang up (5)

3 Belgian city (5)

4 Release after a security has been paid (4)

5 Roman soldier (9)

6 Proximity (9)

10 Change the order or arrangement of (9)

11 Craft used outside the Earth's atmosphere (9)

12 Animal's den (4)

14 Dismal, dour (4)

19 Semi-precious stone with streaked colouring (5)

20 Paragon (5)

22 Necessitate (4)

143

Across

1 Physically strong (6)
4 Formerly the basic unit of money in Spain (6)
7 Misbehave (4,2)
9 Disorder of the central nervous system (8)
11 Young girl (4)
14 Holder on a boat that acts as a fulcrum for rowing (7)
15 Part of a necklace (4)
16 The smallest quantity (4)
17 Whenever (7)
18 Called on the phone (4)
21 City in southern Japan on Kyushu (8)
22 Small meat and vegetable turnover of Indian origin (6)
24 Uses jointly (6)
25 Withdraw from an organisation (6)

Down

1 Disgust (5)
2 Pulse vegetables (5)
3 Small coin (3)
4 Abdominal inflammation (11)
5 More screechy (9)
6 Nautical term used in hailing (4)
8 Biblical entrance to heaven (6,5)
10 Ruler of a Muslim country (6)
12 List of items for discussion (6)
13 Effervescent mixer drink (4,5)
19 Dwelling (5)
20 Tomb (5)
21 Tidings (4)
23 Expert (3)

144

Across

1 Job (6)

5 Beetle considered divine by ancient Egyptians (6)

8 Man-eating giant (4)

9 Quantity (6)

10 Judge tentatively (5)

11 Follow instruction (4)

12 Not in action (4)

13 To the opposite side (6)

15 Methods (4)

17 Noise made by a snake (4)

19 Plant similar to the rhodo-dendron (6)

20 Part of a lock (4)

21 Fête (4)

22 First Greek letter (5)

24 Direction leading to the centre (6)

25 Waterside plant (4)

26 Overabundance (6)

27 Marriage partner (6)

Down

2 Branch of mathematics (7)

3 Mournful poem (5)

4 Contest of speed (4)

5 Coast (8)

6 Do away with (7)

7 Swimmers (7)

14 Acting game, popular at Christmas (8)

15 Location of a series of pages on the internet (7)

16 Fill to satisfaction (7)

18 Vendors (7)

21 Greta ___, film star (1905–90) (5)

23 Succeed in an examination (4)

145

Across

4 Of legs, to take out of a folded position (7)

7 Go beyond a time limit (7)

8 Undersides of shoes (5)

9 Characterised by dignity and propriety (5)

10 Bird similar to an ostrich (3)

11 Act of immoderate indulgence (5)

12 Cylindrical masses of earth voided by burrowing creatures (9)

14 Underwater warship (9)

17 Actions (5)

18 Be in possession of (3)

19 Diadem (5)

21 Flexible twig of a willow tree (5)

22 Form a mental picture (7)

23 Agitate, excite (5,2)

Down

1 Foreman (4)

2 Bracing atmosphere by the coast (3,3)

3 Person who comes before one in time (11)

4 Not if (6)

5 Connected to a computer network (6)

6 Apprehension about what is going to happen (8)

8 Fairly large, significant (11)

12 Extraordinarily good or great (8)

13 Part of the eye (6)

15 Mythical monster said to live in watery places like swamps (6)

16 Slanted lettering (6)

20 Plant family which includes the maple (4)

146

Across

1 Maltreater (6)

3 Prickly desert plant (6)

7 Happening again and again, tediously (11)

10 Kept apart (8)

11 Egg on (4)

13 Portable light (5)

14 Public announcement of a proposed marriage (5)

18 Curved gateway (4)

19 Crystalline rock that can be cut for jewellery (8)

21 Ill-fated (4-7)

22 Craftsman who makes cloth (6)

23 In one's place of residence (2,4)

Down

1 Cowardly (6)

2 Way in (8)

4 Highly excited (4)

5 Small pouch for shampoo, etc (6)

6 Speak, articulate (5)

8 Long flexible snout (9)

9 Taxing of one's energy (9)

12 Official travel permit (8)

15 Capital of Poland (6)

16 Heave, regurgitate (5)

17 Sewing tool (6)

20 Cassette (4)

147

Across

1 Construct again (7)
6 Public transport vehicle (3)
8 Sprang up (5)
9 Alike (7)
10 Bread-raising agent (5)
11 Erroneous (8)
13 Sharpshooter (6)
15 Most recent (6)
18 Expired (8)
19 Canonised person (5)
21 Desirous of a drink (7)
22 Superficial abrasion (5)
23 Donkey (3)
24 Slackened (7)

Down

2 Issue of a newspaper (7)
3 Unlucky (3-5)
4 Become less light (6)
5 Australian term for a young kangaroo (4)
6 Due to, on account of (7)
7 Instrument for measuring the angle between stars (7)
12 Fabric (8)
13 Variety of mandarin orange (7)
14 Batting team (7)
16 Enfold (7)
17 Court clown (6)
20 Nipple (4)

148

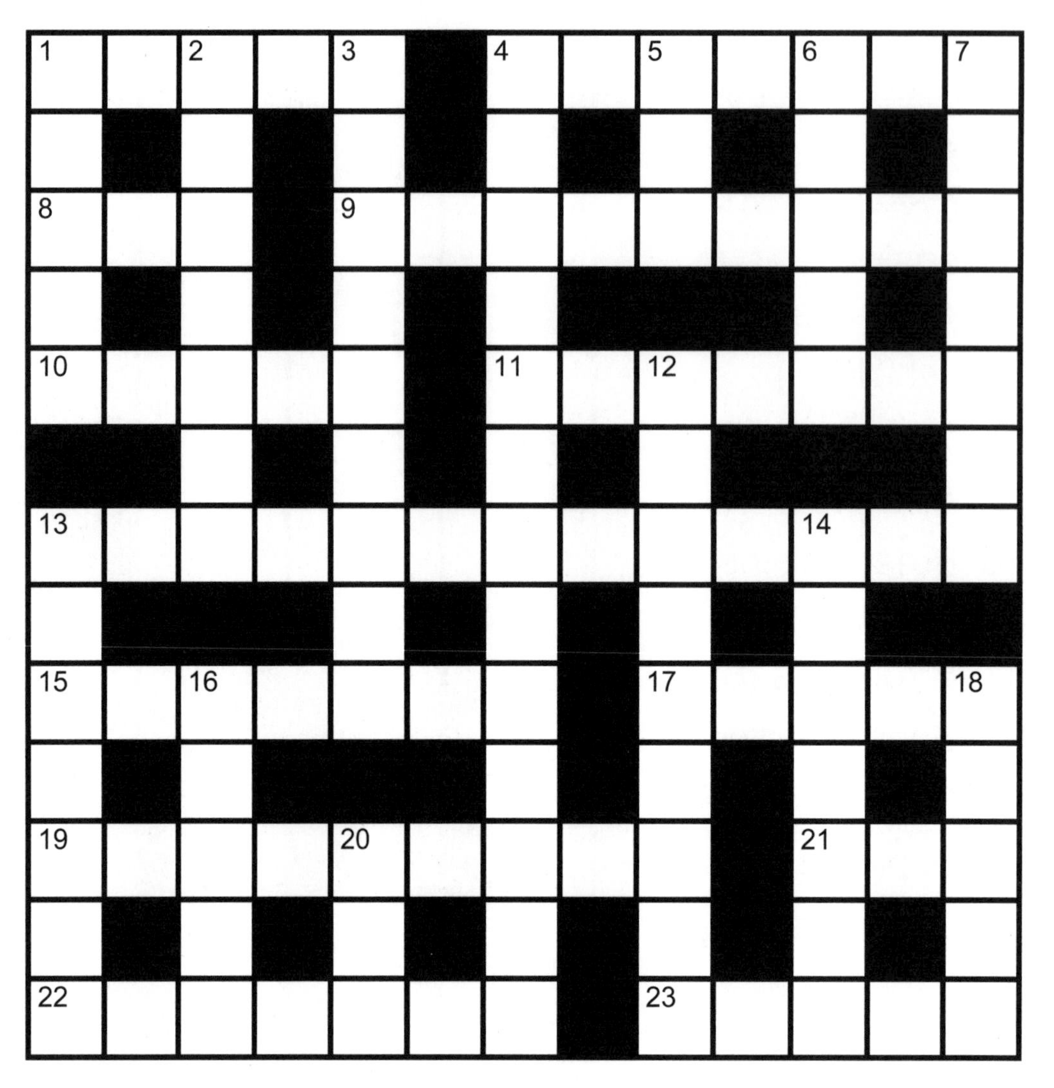

Across

1 Australian wild dog (5)

4 Having a high-pitched sound like that of a mouse (7)

8 Grandmother (3)

9 Rose, sweet briar (9)

10 Dame Nellie ___, Australian operatic soprano (5)

11 Clergyman's salary (7)

13 Cultured, appealing to those having worldly knowledge and refinement (13)

15 Everlasting (7)

17 Interprets words (5)

19 Come about, happen (9)

21 Bronze (3)

22 Come down (7)

23 Wears out (5)

Down

1 Jeans fabric (5)

2 Designed to reduce or prevent sliding (3-4)

3 Being in force (9)

4 Marked by excessive complacency (4-9)

5 Container for ashes (3)

6 A Town like ___, Nevil Shute novel later made into a film (5)

7 Gave way, relinquished control over (7)

12 Wrong (9)

13 Extracted (metals) by heating (7)

14 Betrayer of one's country (7)

16 Hands out playing-cards (5)

18 Air cavity in the skull (5)

20 Girl's name (3)

149

Across

1 Alter (6)
7 Encircle (8)
8 Academic test (4)
10 Elongated cluster of flowers (6)
11 Parch (4)
12 Linger (5)
13 In a murderous frenzy (7)
16 Flop (3)
17 Perfumed (7)
19 Stonecutter (5)
21 Coloured part of the eye (4)
23 Crown (6)
25 Fury (4)
26 Resistance (8)
27 Tendons (6)

Down

1 Ornamental climbing plant (8)
2 Partly open (4)
3 Organic compound (5)
4 Free from tears (3-4)
5 Flip (a coin, for example) (4)
6 Imbalanced (6)
9 Head nurse (6)
13 Partially opened flower (3)
14 Someone who skims across ice (6)
15 Humanity, sympathy (8)
16 Cul-de-sac (4-3)
18 Point where two lines meet or intersect (6)
20 Projecting edge of a roof (5)
22 Front part of the human leg below the knee (4)
24 Female horse (4)

150

Across

1 Ski-race over a winding course (6)

7 Lively (8)

8 Actor, ___ Baldwin, former husband of Kim Basinger (4)

10 Looked for (6)

11 Rise upward into the air (4)

12 Atomic exploding device (1-4)

13 Informing by words (7)

17 Feel of a surface (7)

19 Round objects used in games (5)

21 Gives assistance (4)

23 Country, capital Ankara (6)

25 Appear (4)

26 Commercial flight companies (8)

27 Higher in rank (6)

Down

1 Informal photograph (8)

2 Imitates (4)

3 Oval fruit with a very large seed (5)

4 Number, XV in Roman numerals (7)

5 Tatters (4)

6 Delay (6)

9 Dedicate (6)

14 Exits (6)

15 Filaments from a web spun by a spider (8)

16 Act as if (7)

18 Magical potion (6)

20 Pasture (5)

22 Lustrous material (4)

24 Abominable snowman (4)

151

Across

1 Gardening scissors (6)

7 Internet site where users communicate in real time (4,4)

8 Go in search of (6)

10 Sliding container in a piece of furniture (6)

11 Short formal piece of writing (5)

13 Becomes angry (coll) (4,3)

16 Combats (7)

17 Gasps for breath (5)

20 Song or hymn of mourning (6)

22 Period of play in cricket (6)

24 Reaction (8)

25 Shade-giving bonnet (3,3)

Down

1 Lithe, limber (6)

2 All the time (4)

3 Fastener with a threaded shank (5)

4 One who trains or exhibits animals (7)

5 Opera song (4)

6 Capable of thinking and expressing oneself clearly (8)

9 Begin (5)

12 Brine (8)

14 Discolour (5)

15 Coming together (7)

18 Small stamp or seal on a ring (6)

19 Exists (5)

21 Catch sight of (4)

23 One twelfth of a foot (4)

152

Across

1 Adequate quantity or supply (11)

9 Discontinue (5)

10 Alcoholic brew (3)

11 Workmanship (5)

12 Rolls (5)

13 Clapping (8)

16 Disagreement (8)

18 Radiance (5)

21 Country, capital Madrid (5)

22 Acquired (3)

23 Mother-of-pearl (5)

24 Substance that stimulates love or desire (11)

Down

2 Miserable (7)

3 Relating to reality (7)

4 Makes sore by rubbing (6)

5 Perpendicular (5)

6 Seat (5)

7 Study of ancient people through their material remains (11)

8 Doggedness, perseverance (11)

14 Edible black marine bivalves (7)

15 Meeting for boat races (7)

17 Off, sour (6)

19 Arise (3,2)

20 Adult male singing voice (5)

153

Across

1 Against (4)
3 Polite behaviour (8)
7 Clergyman's title (8)
8 After that (4)
9 Nova ___, Canadian peninsula (6)
11 Dried grape (6)
13 Keen on (4)
14 Dais (5)
15 Army unit of two or more divisions (5)
17 Hill of sand (4)
19 Ship's officer who keeps accounts (6)
22 Follow-up (6)
23 Cloak-like garment (4)
24 Administrative district of a nation (8)
25 Plumage (8)
26 Unit of length equal to 1760 yards (4)

Down

1 Again but in a new or different way (6)
2 Motionlessness (7)
3 Reduce to ashes (7)
4 Below (5)
5 For all (music) (5)
6 On the Origin of ___, work by Charles Darwin (7)
10 Fireplace (5)
12 Make amends (5)
14 Highly seasoned meat stuffed in a casing (7)
15 Traditions (7)
16 Mass celebrated for the dead (7)
18 Sheep's coat (6)
20 Exhausted (5)
21 Indian currency unit (5)

154

Across

1 What you see is what you get – in computing terms! (7)

8 Pear-shaped fruit (7)

9 Pals (7)

10 Women (6)

12 Victim of ridicule or pranks (6)

13 Relating to the land (11)

17 Level a charge against (6)

20 Sickness (6)

23 Cloth used when washing-up (7)

24 Raised in rank (7)

25 Slim or small (7)

Down

1 Pancake batter baked in an iron implement (6)

2 Rotating shaft (7)

3 Cringe (5)

4 Short intake of breath (4)

5 Brag (5)

6 Key ___, 1948 film (5)

7 Hat tied under the chin (6)

11 Leather with a napped surface (5)

12 Glossy fabric (5)

14 Certain of (7)

15 Sponsor, investor (6)

16 Carnivorous burrowing mammal (6)

18 Durable aromatic wood (5)

19 Saline (5)

21 Church passage (5)

22 ___ and ends (4)

155

Across

1 Snatches (5)
4 Pre-release screening for a select audience (7)
8 In a graceful or stylish manner (9)
9 French river (5)
10 Sepulchral monument (9)
13 Object thrown in athletic competitions (6)
14 Crustacean with seven pairs of legs (6)
16 Expressing ridicule that wounds (9)
19 Helicopter propeller (5)
20 Characteristic (9)
22 One of the three superpowers in Nineteen Eighty-Four (7)
23 Church council (5)

Down

1 Unexpected piece of good fortune (7)
2 Manager of a business or school (13)
3 Mix of rain and snow (5)
4 Food in a pastry shell (3)
5 Tests of proficiency (abbr) (5)
6 Observation of one's own mental and emotional processes (13)
7 John ___, film actor who played tough heroes (5)
11 Expels (5)
12 Russian pancake (5)
15 Deprive of by deceit (7)
16 Trap for birds or small mammals (5)
17 Farewell remark (5)
18 Green salad vegetable (5)
21 Large nation (inits) (3)

156

Across

1 Mouldable synthetic substance (7)

8 Italian rice dish (7)

9 Musical toy (7)

10 Loophole (6)

12 Card game (6)

13 Sand, soda and lime compound, pulverised into an abrasive powder (6,5)

17 Stings (6)

20 Fertilised egg (6)

23 Enmity (3,4)

24 Restraining straps (7)

25 Water tank (7)

Down

1 Drive from behind (6)

2 Non-professional (7)

3 Lining of the stomach of a ruminant used as food (5)

4 Pack to capacity (4)

5 ___ Wilde, playwright (5)

6 Valuable violin (informally) (5)

7 Player who delivers the ball to the batsman (6)

11 Hinged lifting tool (5)

12 Brass instrument without valves (5)

14 Act of assistance (7)

15 Seat of the faculty of reason (6)

16 Mischievous ugly demon (6)

18 Terminate (5)

19 Striped cat (5)

21 Boys, men (5)

22 Flat round object (4)

157

Across

1 Woolly-headed (6)
5 Acute (5)
9 Repairs to the highway (9)
10 Chores (5)
11 Serialised TV programme (4,5)
13 Large edible predatory eel (6)
15 Short sleep (6)
19 Contract to do (9)
21 Nigerian monetary unit (5)
22 Disputative (9)
24 Childish word for scrumptious (5)
25 Be undecided (6)

Down

2 Roman goddess of the hunt (5)
3 Depleted (3)
4 Moved rapidly (6)
5 Provide with nourishment (7)
6 Haywire (5)
7 Announcement distributed to the media (5,7)
8 Long race run over open terrain (5,7)
12 Domestic swine (3)
14 To the same degree (7)
16 Choose (3)
17 Revised before printing (6)
18 Musical half-note (5)
20 On your own (5)
23 Bowel (3)

158

Across

1 Clicking pendulum indicating the tempo of a piece of music (9)
5 Catch sight of (3)
7 Performer who moves to music (6)
8 Ceremonial procession (6)
10 Multicoloured (4)
11 Appearance of a place (7)
13 Take away a part from, diminish (7)
17 Male child of your spouse and a former partner (7)
19 Less than average tide (4)
21 Mass of snow which permanently covers the land (6)
22 Laugh at or mock (6)
23 Nitrogen, for example (3)
24 Fastener used on clothing (5,4)

Down

1 Manufactured (4)
2 Game played with racquets (6)
3 Not at the scheduled time (7)
4 Fill with optimism (5)
5 Lines on which musical notes are written (6)
6 All people (8)
9 Minimal wear item (1-6)
12 Going from one side to the other (8)
14 Admit one's guilt (7)
15 Precious stones (6)
16 Lasso (6)
18 Skin covering the top of the head (5)
20 Despatch (4)

159

Across

1 Arrived (4)

3 Primitive wind instrument (3-5)

9 Projecting moulding (7)

10 Language, jargon (5)

11 Construe in the wrong way (12)

14 Ms Braun, Hitler's mistress (3)

16 Flowerless plants that reproduce by spores (5)

17 2240 pounds (3)

18 Not on (12)

21 Fire-raising (5)

22 Italian dumplings (7)

23 Collect discarded material (8)

24 Russian emperor (4)

Down

1 Green salad fruit (8)

2 Distinguishing features (5)

4 Bladed chopping tool (3)

5 Most favourable placing at the start of a race (4,8)

6 Sharply biting or acrid especially in taste (7)

7 Mixture of fog and smoke (4)

8 Meaning (12)

12 Eagle's nest (5)

13 Falling short of some prescribed norm (8)

15 Loss of memory (7)

19 Informal term for dollars (5)

20 Celebration of the Eucharist (4)

22 Prevent from speaking out (3)

160

Across

1 Subsist on a meagre allowance (5)

4 Timeless (7)

8 Examiner of accounts (7)

9 Predict from an omen (5)

10 Fight (3-2)

11 Former (3-4)

12 Shield (6)

13 Look up to (6)

16 Liquorice-flavoured herb (7)

18 Endure, put up with (5)

20 Educate in a skill (5)

21 Burn bubble (7)

22 Exact (7)

23 Fashion (5)

Down

1 Crustlike surfaces of healing wounds (5)

2 Not fixed or known in advance (13)

3 Pit produced by wear or weathering (7)

4 Orange root vegetable (6)

5 Humble (5)

6 To an important degree (13)

7 Funeral procession (7)

12 Set in motion (5,2)

14 Send away (7)

15 Comestible (6)

17 Boredom (5)

19 Funereal lament (5)

161

Across

1 Snag (5)
4 Drop sharply (7)
8 Egg cells (3)
9 Has in mind (5)
10 Sharp part of a knife (5)
11 In a cheerful manner (10)
13 Slip away (6)
15 Clothes cupboard (6)
18 Warning given in error (5,5)
22 Deport from a country (5)
23 Make a thrusting forward movement (5)
24 Grow older (3)
25 Emanating from stars (7)
26 Holds fast (5)

Down

1 Writer of music (8)
2 Disreputable wanderer (5)
3 Woman who invites guests to a social event (7)
4 Local church community (6)
5 Characteristic of a city (5)
6 Childhood disease (7)
7 Swarm (4)
12 First courses (8)
14 Greed (7)
16 Brochure (7)
17 Salted roe of a sturgeon (6)
19 Alloy of iron and carbon (5)
20 Mood disorder (5)
21 Professional charges (4)

162

Across

1 Lawyer who speaks in the higher courts of law (9)

8 Distinctive smell (5)

9 Drinking vessel (5)

10 Bring together (5)

11 Castrated bull (5)

12 Strong, tightly twisted cotton thread (5)

14 Holiday town (6)

16 Population count (6)

20 Attack on all sides (5)

23 Make speeches (5)

25 Carriageways (5)

26 Sugar frosting (5)

27 Panorama (5)

28 Process or result of becoming less or smaller (9)

Down

1 Phoney (5)

2 Literate people (7)

3 Underwriter (7)

4 Removing (6)

5 French composer (1875–1937) (5)

6 Fillip, incentive (5)

7 Receptacles for shopping (7)

13 Hostelry (3)

14 Refuse (7)

15 Lyric poem (3)

17 Wearing away (7)

18 Staying power (7)

19 Pencil mark remover (6)

21 Alarm (5)

22 Attempts (5)

24 Bird of prey (5)

163

Across

1 Indian lute (5)
4 Curvaceous (7)
7 Visitor from space? (inits) (3)
8 Caribbean country (5)
9 Ultimate clients for which a thing is intended (3,5)
10 Japanese rice dish (5)
12 Got ready (8)
16 Drink (8)
18 Morsel (5)
20 Having a wish for something (8)
21 Adipose (5)
22 Livestock enclosure (3)
23 Pan used for frying foods (7)
24 Appetising (5)

Down

1 Climbing plants that produce fragrant flowers (5,4)
2 Child learning to walk (7)
3 Native of Moscow, for example (7)
4 Origin (6)
5 Pestilence (6)
6 Spring-loaded door fastener (5)
11 Make stronger or more marked (9)
13 Boldly resisting authority or an opposing force (7)
14 Extends overgenerous preferential treatment to (7)
15 Consortium of companies formed to limit competition (6)
17 Excepted (6)
19 Writing implement (5)

164

Across

1 Tightly curled and unopened flower (7)

5 Perform without preparation (2-3)

8 To stretch out (3)

9 Course of appetisers in an Italian meal (9)

10 Empower (5)

12 Long fishes (4)

14 Destroy the peace of (7)

16 Not this! (4)

18 Soap froth (4)

20 Ability to walk steadily on the deck of a ship (3,4)

22 Location (4)

23 Bohemian dance (5)

25 More favourable position (9)

26 Deciduous tree (3)

27 Develop fully (5)

28 Add sugar to (7)

Down

1 Vote back into office (2-5)

2 Unwavering (9)

3 Favouring one person or side over another (6)

4 Go out with (4)

6 Boxlike containers in a piece of furniture (7)

7 Footwear that covers the lower legs (5)

11 Adult male deer (4)

13 High-spirited (9)

15 Offshore territory (4)

17 Adolescent (7)

19 Itinerant Australian labourer (7)

21 Globe (6)

22 Step (5)

24 Flexible containers (4)

165

Across

1 Edible decapod (6)
7 Against the current (8)
8 Type of cobra (3)
9 Dire warning (6)
10 Blow delivered with an open hand (4)
11 Stony hillside (5)
13 Storage locker (7)
15 Enclosed (7)
17 Aromatic plants used in cookery (5)
21 Equipment for the reproduction of sound (2-2)
22 Earth colour (6)
23 Ignited (3)
24 Location next to the warmest place in the house (8)
25 Alternative name for the voice box (6)

Down

1 Shelters from light (6)
2 Carnivorous bird, such as the eagle (6)
3 Fruit pulp (5)
4 Receptacle used by smokers (7)
5 Immaculately clean and unused (8)
6 Control (6)
12 Type of make-up (8)
14 Start out on a sea voyage (3,4)
16 Place where something begins (6)
18 Property consisting of houses and land (6)
19 Phrase structure (6)
20 Chamfer (5)

166

Across

1 Shouts of approval (6)

4 Thin sliver of wood (6)

7 Mother superior (6)

8 Formal exposition (8)

12 Steps consisting of two parallel members connected by rungs (6)

14 Money chest (6)

15 Edna ___, Irish writer (born in 1932) (6)

16 Talk like a baby (6)

18 Slaughterhouse (8)

22 Mark of infamy (6)

23 Flamboyantly elaborate, showy (6)

24 Bone of the forearm (6)

Down

1 Partially burn (4)

2 Protective fold of skin (6)

3 Female sibling (6)

4 Free from danger (4)

5 Cobbler's stand (4)

6 Subdue (4)

9 Hawaiian greeting (5)

10 Stinking (6)

11 Gigantic African and Australian tree with edible fruits (6)

13 Bring into play (5)

16 Treasurer at a college or university (6)

17 In arrears (6)

18 Zealous (4)

19 Bathroom fixtures (4)

20 Wild gathering involving excessive drinking and promiscuity (4)

21 Agitates the air (4)

167

Across

1 Malignant growth or tumour (6)

5 Reaping hook (6)

8 Child's horse (4)

9 Merry-go-round (8)

10 Bathroom fixture (5)

11 Christening (7)

14 Sickness (6)

15 Make certain (6)

17 Animal product used as a furniture polish (7)

19 Breakfast rasher (5)

21 Characteristic of a woman (8)

23 Item used to carry many cups at once (4)

24 Expend in hope of profit (6)

25 English landscape painter (1775–1851) (6)

Down

2 Find repugnant (9)

3 Affectation of being demure in a provocative way (7)

4 Large stone (4)

5 Pennant (8)

6 Be important (5)

7 Side sheltered from the wind (3)

12 Person who takes the place of another (9)

13 One resigned to the inevitable (8)

16 Break into many pieces (7)

18 Skid (5)

20 Adroit (4)

22 Long period of time (3)

168

Across

1 Fluid circulating through the body (11)
7 Large northern deer (3)
8 Hopeless undertaking (4,5)
10 Beginning of time (4,3)
12 Cause an engine to stop (5)
15 Incumbency (6)
16 Arched (6)
17 Finger next to the thumb (5)
20 Simulated rather than really existing (7)
23 Tearing down so as to make flat with the ground (9)
25 Children's game (3)
26 Proportionate, matching (11)

Down

1 Browbeat (5)
2 Frequently, poetically (3)
3 Followed clandestinely (8)
4 Level betting (5)
5 Means for communicating information (5)
6 Experienced, competent (7)
9 Bathing resort (3)
11 Course (5)
13 Fortune-teller's pack of cards (5)
14 Chance event (8)
15 Accolade (7)
18 Impurities left in the final drops of a liquid (5)
19 Woody part of plants (5)
21 Canton in Switzerland, home to William Tell (3)
22 Founded upon law (5)
24 Floral garland (3)

169

Across

4 Aviator who assists the captain of a plane (2-5)
8 Accumulate (5)
9 Entertainer (9)
10 Military fabric (5)
11 Disposed to believe on little evidence (9)
13 Unpleasant odour (6)
16 Perplexing riddle (6)
20 Ocean-going (9)
23 Wireless (5)
24 Native Australian (9)
25 Consecrate (5)
26 Series of rooms where works of art are exhibited (7)

Down

1 Male donkey (7)
2 Decorative undersheet on a bed (7)
3 Savoury jelly (5)
4 Restriction on being outside (6)
5 Bring out for display (7)
6 West Indian dance (5)
7 Limited periods of time (5)
12 Consumption (3)
14 Foot digit (3)
15 Extremely poisonous substance (7)
17 Member of an army (7)
18 Contrition (7)
19 In a flippant manner (6)
20 Informal language (5)
21 Coral reef (5)
22 Small compact-bodied almost completely aquatic bird (5)

170

Across

1 Travel by foot (4)

3 Completed (8)

9 Plants, often with unusual flowers (7)

10 Copy on thin paper (5)

11 Gather into a ruffle (5)

12 Transports (7)

13 French port city on the Loire (6)

15 Type of firearm (3,3)

17 Direction indicator (7)

18 Entice (5)

20 Distressed (5)

21 Car used as a taxi (7)

22 Inn (8)

23 Live-action film about a piglet (4)

Down

1 Pertussis (8,5)

2 Informal term for money (5)

4 Ant or beetle, for example (6)

5 Sporadic (12)

6 Making warm (7)

7 Item of bedroom furniture (8,5)

8 Gossip (6-6)

14 Goddess of retribution (7)

16 Chemical with the same formula but a different structure (6)

19 Birthplace of Mohammed (5)

171

Across

4 Grown-up (6)

7 American state in the Rocky Mountains (8)

8 In a tidy and ordered way (6)

9 Humidity (8)

10 Rental (5)

12 Spare time (7)

16 Someone who breaks free (7)

19 Cinema attendant (5)

23 Mariner (8)

24 Military trainees (6)

25 Whole and intact (8)

26 Stick of wax with a central wick (6)

Down

1 Give to a charity (6)

2 Changes shape as via computer animation (6)

3 Biblical tower intended to reach to heaven (5)

4 Colossus (7)

5 Expresses gratitude (6)

6 Hair curler (6)

10 Be prostrate (3)

11 Bow (3)

13 Word expressing disgust (3)

14 Head of corn (3)

15 Print anew (7)

17 World's largest desert (6)

18 Climb up (6)

20 Ms Stone, actress in the Basic Instinct films (6)

21 Number represented by the Roman XI (6)

22 Jewish spiritual leader (5)

172

Across

1 Evaluate (6)
5 Disperse (6)
8 Consecrate (6)
9 Protestant layman who assists the minister (6)
10 Word of surprise (3)
11 Rate of travel (5)
13 Give or restore confidence in (8)
15 Unconsciousness induced by drugs (8)
16 Cape (5)
19 Pen point (3)
21 Popular drink (6)
22 Type of thorny tree (6)
23 Area set back or indented (6)
24 Ocean floor (6)

Down

2 Accumulation of refuse (9)
3 Circumvent (5)
4 Musical composition with words (4)
5 Obliquely (8)
6 Take in, understand (7)
7 Over, finished (4)
12 Thin syrup made from pomegranate juice (9)
13 Impetuosity (8)
14 Minor skirmish (7)
17 Andean mammal (5)
18 Mark of a wound (4)
20 Lowest adult male singing voice (4)

173

Across

1 Adult male bird (4)

3 Interval in the working day (3,5)

9 Marine fowl (7)

10 Lustre (5)

11 Day in spring on which the Resurrection is celebrated (6,6)

14 Not in good health (3)

16 Occasions for buying at lower prices (5)

17 Mature female deer (3)

18 Californian port, site of the Golden Gate Bridge (3,9)

21 Plea of being elsewhere (5)

22 Slaughter (7)

23 Hiring (for work) (8)

24 Had existence (4)

Down

1 Lipstick, for example (8)

2 Bedlam (5)

4 Come to a halt (3)

5 Note on which is printed a person's name and company information (8,4)

6 Green gem (7)

7 Male sovereign (4)

8 Branching out (12)

12 Spicy tomato sauce (5)

13 Paraffin oil (8)

15 Inclining (7)

19 Roofing material (5)

20 Teatime treat (4)

22 Metal container (3)

174

Across

1 Despise (6)

4 Colourless watery fluid of blood (6)

7 Figure of speech expressing a similarity (8)

9 Bill of fare (4)

10 Rend (3)

12 Behave towards (5)

13 Lucky (7)

14 Arrangement (6)

15 Not so warm (6)

17 Motivate (7)

21 Forum in ancient Greece (5)

23 God of the sun, also known as Helios (3)

24 Cooking utensils (4)

25 Functionary (8)

26 Happens again (6)

27 Puts off, discourages (6)

Down

1 Boundary (5)

2 Female stage performer (7)

3 Surmisal (10)

4 Danger (5)

5 Paces (5)

6 Into pieces (7)

8 Globe (3)

11 Expressing disapproval or contempt (10)

14 Indoor shoe (7)

16 Resembling a lion (7)

18 Of sound (5)

19 Areas within a house (5)

20 Fairy (3)

22 Book of maps (5)

175

Across

4 Seed often used on bread rolls (6)

7 Italian sponge cake, coffee and brandy dessert (8)

8 Desolate (6)

9 Release after a security has been paid (4)

10 Bounder (3)

12 Cold vegetable dish (5)

13 Imaginary water nymph (7)

16 Climbing plant (7)

18 Formal title used when addressing a woman (5)

21 Flow back (3)

22 Ensnare (4)

23 Kitchen appliance, oven (6)

25 Duplicitous (3-5)

26 Moral principles (6)

Down

1 Stout-bodied insect which produces a loud, chirping sound (6)

2 Decoration hung in a home (9)

3 The letter 'H' written as a word (5)

4 Quieted and brought under control (7)

5 Title (3)

6 Breakfast food (6)

11 Unprejudiced (9)

12 Pouch (3)

14 Barrier which contains the flow of water (3)

15 Arid regions of the world (7)

17 Give an account in words (6)

19 Rouse from slumber (6)

20 Chief monk (5)

24 Ornamental carp (3)

176

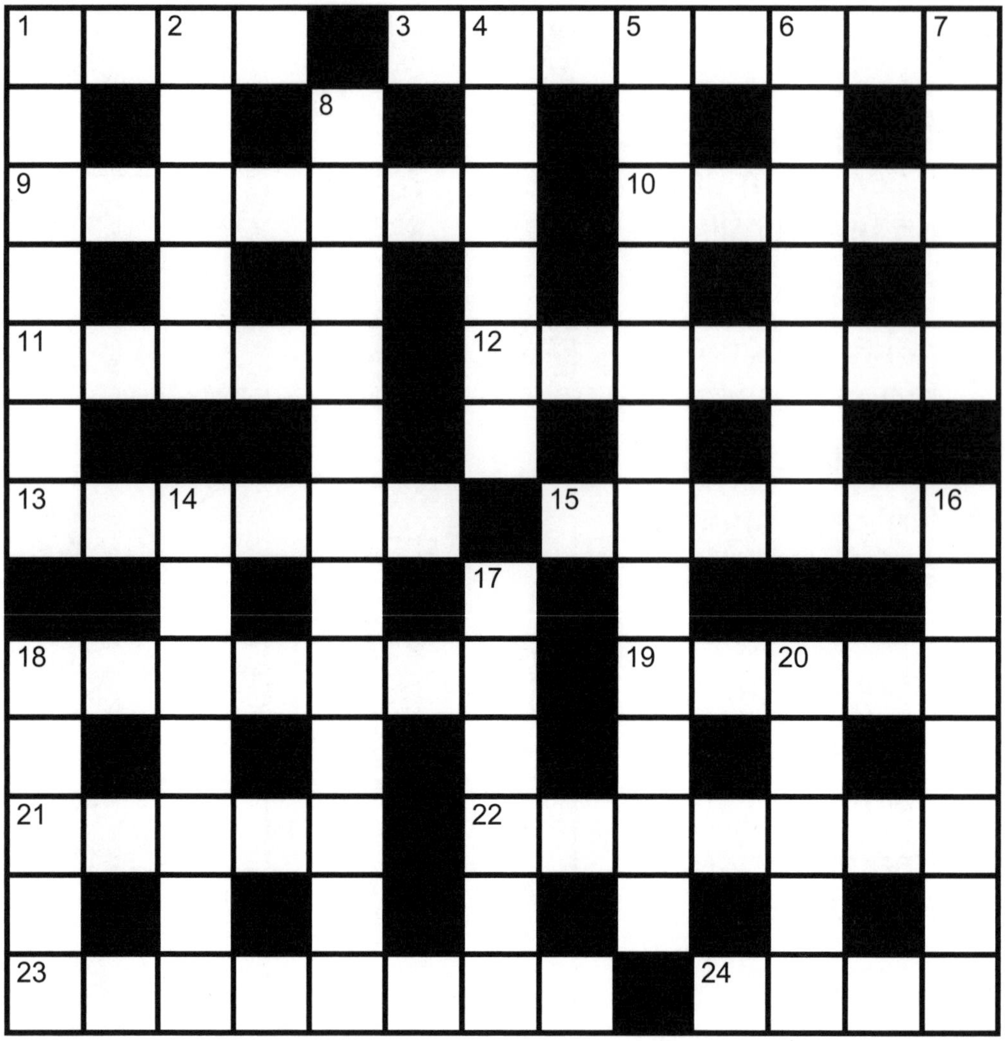

Across

1 Burn without flame (4)

3 Exaggerated masculinity (8)

9 Dumbfounding (7)

10 Confused scuffle (5)

11 Wasp's defence (5)

12 Be enough (7)

13 Israeli monetary unit (6)

15 Fist fighters (6)

18 Confectionery made from sugar, butter and nuts (7)

19 Japanese verse form (5)

21 Lukewarm (5)

22 Vestige (7)

23 Take too much medication (8)

24 Dull pain (4)

Down

1 Spectacles (7)

2 Animal similar to the giraffe (5)

4 Summer month (6)

5 Place where you are just as comfortable as in your own residence (4,4,4)

6 St Andrew's cross (7)

7 Abnormally fat (5)

8 Determined, resolute (6-6)

14 Instance (7)

16 Travel back and forth between two points (7)

17 Beads produced by oysters (6)

18 Courtyard (5)

20 ___ Asimov, science-fiction writer (5)

177

Across

1 Stroke lovingly (6)
4 Bordering (6)
9 Lean back (7)
10 Endeavour (7)
11 Surgeon's pincers (7)
12 Compass point (5)
14 Lofty proud gait (5)
15 Jovial (5)
17 Canadian policeman, usually on horseback (7)
19 Abatement (7)
21 Constructing or forming a web, as if by weaving (7)
22 Thoroughfare (6)
23 Baby's plaything (6)

Down

1 Decanter (6)
2 Tubular wind instrument with eight finger-holes (8)
3 County (5)
5 Afar (7)
6 Mosque official (4)
7 Sudden, usually temporary malfunction of equipment (6)
8 Act of ascertaining an amount (11)
13 Curtail (8)
14 Medical instrument used to inject (7)
15 Quagmire (6)
16 Association of sports teams (6)
18 Far beyond the norm (5)
20 Disparaging remark (4)

178

Across

1 Rich, buttery sponge with a close texture (7,4)

7 Dots in a text showing suppression of words (8)

8 Tibetan or Mongolian priest (4)

9 Hearty and lusty, crude (6)

11 Arm covering (6)

13 Emblem (5)

14 Corrode (5)

17 Design made of small pieces of coloured stone or glass (6)

20 Blasphemed (6)

22 Star which ejects material (4)

23 Situation, set-up (8)

24 Impoverished, destitute (11)

Down

1 More modest (6)

2 Have actual being (5)

3 Arrange into a different shape or layout (7)

4 Abnormal swellings on the body (5)

5 Ms Minogue (5)

6 Astonished (6)

10 Wanders about (5)

12 Actress Linda, who played Krystle Carrington in Dynasty (5)

14 Wife of a duke (7)

15 Rectifies (6)

16 Abominable (6)

18 Semi-precious stone (5)

19 Hindu social class (5)

21 Respond (5)

179

Across

1 Adhesive postal tokens (6)

4 Dark-coloured igneous rock (6)

7 Consciousness of one's own identity (3)

8 Becomes older (4)

9 Vigilant (4-4)

11 Extremely and unpleasantly hot (6)

13 Canine film star (6)

15 Service of china or silverware, used at table (3,3)

18 Treat with excessive indulgence (6)

20 Message of protest signed by many people (8)

22 Molten rock (4)

23 Afternoon meal (3)

24 Lethal (6)

25 Fairy (6)

Down

1 Unforeseen obstacle (4)

2 Artist of consummate skill (6)

3 In next to first place (6)

4 Toward or located in the north (6)

5 Emphasis (6)

6 Being of the same dimensions as an original (4-5)

10 Tendency to stick together (9)

12 Decorate with frosting (3)

14 Bustle (3)

16 Hand-held piece of armour (6)

17 One score and ten (6)

18 Fabric for a painting (6)

19 Navy man (6)

21 Walking-stick (4)

180

Across

1 Acquire for oneself before others can do so (3-4)

5 Tubes (5)

8 Larva of a butterfly or moth (11)

9 Authorises (5)

11 Bloodsucker in folklore (7)

13 Lots and lots (6)

14 Dental decay (6)

17 Drink given to people who are ill (4,3)

18 Breezy (5)

19 Megalithic monument (5,6)

22 Perspiration (5)

23 Burdensome (7)

Down

1 Small flute (7)

2 Consume (3)

3 Confused multitude of things (5-4)

4 Steal something (6)

5 Close friend (3)

6 Vertical structure that divides or separates (9)

7 Arctic marten (5)

10 Person to whom an envelope is written (9)

12 During the intervening time (9)

15 Timidity (7)

16 Small, roofed building affording shade and rest (6)

17 Ecstasy (5)

20 Cereal grass (3)

21 Make the sound of a dove (3)

181

Across

1 Pitch dangerously to one side (6)

4 Marked by practical hard-headed intelligence (6)

7 Water tanker (6)

9 In a direction towards the Orient (8)

11 Bitter sweet (4)

14 Learned person (7)

15 Computer memory unit (4)

16 Hoax (4)

17 Flat area in a series of slopes (7)

18 One who works during a strike (4)

21 Contagious infection of the skin (8)

22 Fix up (6)

24 Forest gods (6)

25 Caused to stop (6)

Down

1 Ancient unit of length (5)

2 Oarsman (5)

3 Biblical first woman (3)

4 Central American capital city (3,8)

5 Practises before an event (9)

6 Declare to be untrue (4)

8 False or misleading clues in a mystery (3,8)

10 Capital of Zambia (6)

12 Psychiatric hospital (6)

13 Winged creature that transmits sleeping sickness (6,3)

19 Move effortlessly (5)

20 Tired of the world (5)

21 Wading bird (4)

23 Epoch, age (3)

182

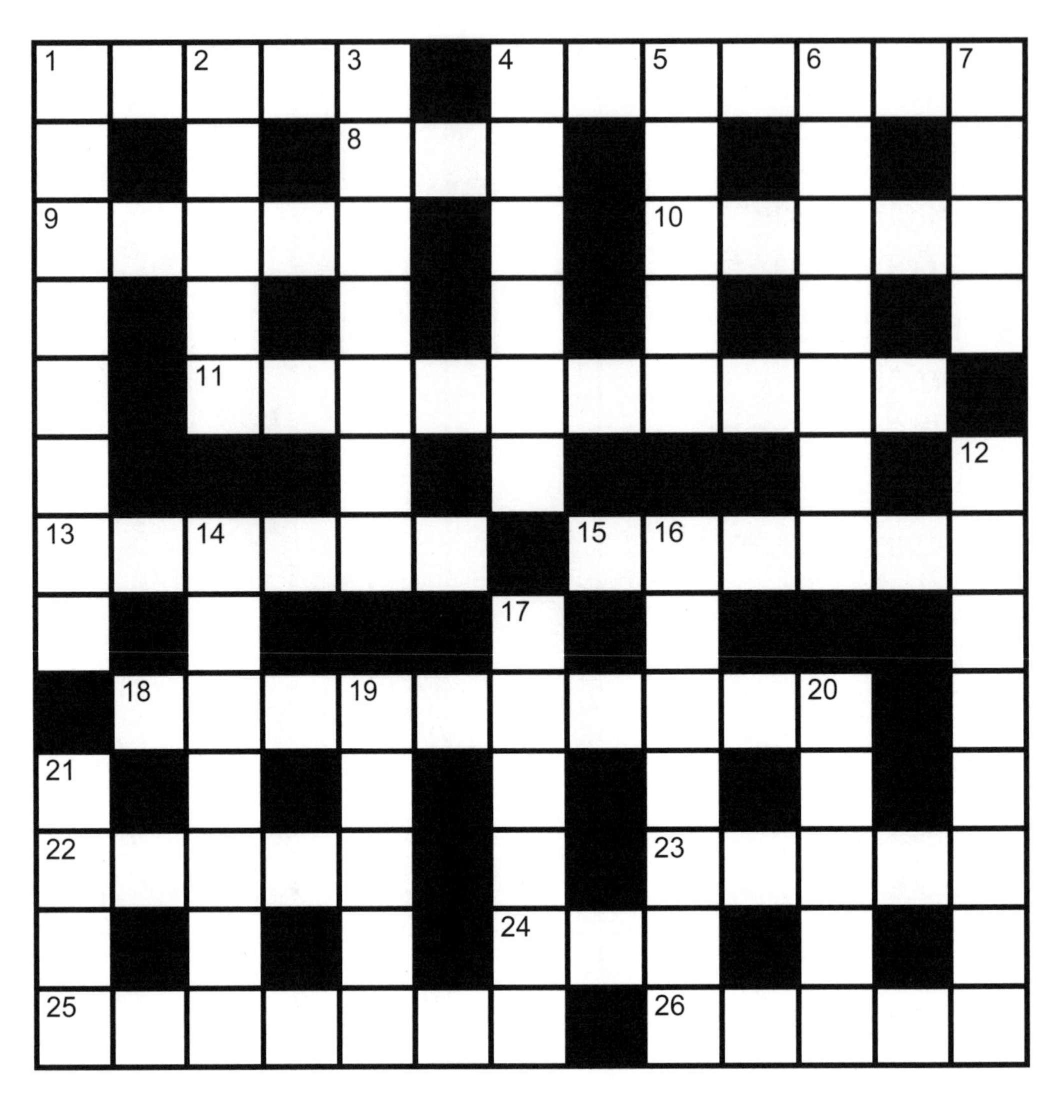

Across

1 Hearty enjoyment (5)

4 Avoiding waste (7)

8 Table-tennis racquet (3)

9 Slabs of grass and grass roots (5)

10 Relative by marriage (2-3)

11 Predisposition in favour of something (10)

13 Drew in by a vacuum (6)

15 Implement for cutting grass (6)

18 Physical or mental inability to do something (10)

22 Adult insect (5)

23 Propels with the foot (5)

24 Reverence (3)

25 Large, ocean-dwelling mammal (3,4)

26 African antelope (5)

Down

1 Upright pole on which a hinged barrier is hung (8)

2 Disrobe (5)

3 Lewd (7)

4 Male reproductive organ of a flower (6)

5 Digression (5)

6 Unlawful (7)

7 Robe (4)

12 US state (8)

14 Musical setting for a religious text (7)

16 Common farmyard bird (7)

17 Plaid associated with Scotland (6)

19 Garlic mayonnaise (5)

20 Popular palm-like houseplant (5)

21 Formal offers at an auction (4)

183

Across

1 Frenzied (5)

7 Mediocre (7)

8 Moldovan monetary unit (3)

9 Fast vehicle for travelling on water (9)

11 Asinine, silly (5)

12 Consignment (8)

16 Land and the buildings on it (8)

20 Love affair (5)

21 Habitual craving (9)

23 Be in debt (3)

24 Filled tortilla (7)

25 Inventories (5)

Down

1 Turning grain into flour (7)

2 Nerve-related (6)

3 Shut (6)

4 Foundation (4)

5 Difficulty (7)

6 Mooring (5)

10 Group considered superior (5)

13 Expel from one's property (5)

14 Reckless or malicious behaviour (7)

15 Weighs down with a heavy load (7)

17 Light shoe with straps (6)

18 Able to absorb fluids (6)

19 Wounding or wittily pointed remarks (5)

22 Graphic symbol (4)

184

Across

1 Maybe (7)
7 Ship's kitchen (6)
9 Money (7)
10 Left over, superfluous (5)
11 Hard outer layer of a fruit (4)
12 Frogman (5)
16 Afterwards (5)
17 Withered (4)
21 Colloquial term for one's ancestry (5)
22 Cup, goblet (7)
23 Country, capital Stockholm (6)
24 Lacking freshness (atmosphere) (7)

Down

1 Popular snack made from maize (7)
2 Beaming (7)
3 Lay out in a line (5)
4 Herb with aromatic finely cut leaves (7)
5 Communion table (5)
6 Keyed into a machine (5)
8 Somewhere to live (9)
13 Pet rodent (7)
14 Act as a go-between (7)
15 First book of the Old Testament (7)
18 Alloy of copper and zinc (5)
19 One stroke over par in golf (5)
20 Frolic, cavort (5)

185

Across

1 Not affected by alcohol (5)

5 Girdle (4)

7 Loosened (6)

8 Heals, makes better (5)

9 Celestial body orbiting another (9)

10 Source of metal (3)

11 Cancellation of civil rights (9)

15 Preventative measure (9)

19 Bunkum (3)

20 Merry-go-round (9)

21 Lift (5)

22 Mountain peak on which Noah's ark came to rest (6)

23 Lairs (4)

24 Root vegetable (5)

Down

1 Area, zone (6)

2 Hairdresser (6)

3 Country, capital Moscow (6)

4 Inform (someone) of a possible future danger (8)

5 Material used to form a hard coating on a porous surface (7)

6 More saline (7)

12 Device providing access to a computer (8)

13 Part of a door fastener (7)

14 Lachrymator (4,3)

16 Knit hose covering the body from the waist to the feet (6)

17 Reach a destination (6)

18 Sculpture (6)

186

Across

1 Meal accompaniment (4,4)

5 Be unsuccessful (4)

7 Registers electronically (7)

8 Underwater missile (7)

9 Grassy plain (7)

11 Depository for displaying objects of historical interest (6)

14 Spherical object (3)

15 Trousers for casual wear (6)

17 Wholly occupy (7)

19 Plunge (7)

22 Jealous (7)

23 Prepares leather (4)

24 Placed very near together (5-3)

Down

1 Condiment, sodium chloride (4)

2 Scattered wreckage (6)

3 Headlong plunge into water (4)

4 Implement used to sharpen razors (5)

5 Fleet of small craft (8)

6 US city famous for gambling (3,5)

10 Chest bones (4)

11 Motion (8)

12 Internal organs, collectively (8)

13 Creeping low plant (4)

16 Traditional Christmas songs (6)

18 Fibre used for making rope (5)

20 Crime syndicates (4)

21 Compass point (4)

187

Across

1 Bag made of hessian or plastic (4)

3 Death of part of the living body (8)

9 Bearer (7)

10 Last letter of the Greek alphabet (5)

11 Old Testament prophet (5)

12 Underhand (6)

14 Phonographic disc (6)

16 Equipment for taking pictures (6)

18 Like better (6)

19 Additional (5)

22 Shores up (5)

23 Cocktail (7)

24 Edgy (8)

25 Fever (4)

Down

1 Type of tree (8)

2 Missives used as birthday or Christmas greetings (5)

4 The act of coming out (6)

5 Chief Brazilian port, famous as a tourist attraction (3,2,7)

6 Dapple (7)

7 Thin strip of wood or metal (4)

8 Chance to buy before it is offered to others (5,7)

13 Lotion used in the treatment of sunburn (8)

15 Inquisitive (7)

17 Small pieces of bread, for example (6)

20 Item (5)

21 Box lightly (4)

188

Across

1 Arctic canoes (6)
8 Excessively devoted to a single faction (3-5)
9 Postpone (3,3)
10 One million million (8)
11 Banquets (6)
12 Embellished with a raised pattern (8)
16 Condition of great disorder (8)
18 National flag (6)
21 Appreciative (8)
23 Thomas ___, US inventor (1847–1931) (6)
24 Psychological suffering (8)
25 Computer that provides access to shared resources (6)

Down

2 Evil or corrupt practice (5)
3 Minute particles of matter (5)
4 Suggestive or persuasive advertising (4,4)
5 Type of food shop (abbr) (4)
6 Register of victims to be eliminated (3,4)
7 Turn into (6)
11 Organs of locomotion and balance in fishes (4)
13 Unwarranted, without foundation (8)
14 Daybreak (4)
15 Copy (7)
17 Rupture in smooth muscle tissue (6)
19 Traveller who uses runners to cross snow (5)
20 Large web-footed bird (5)
22 At liberty (4)

189

Across

1 Went beyond (8)

7 Rationality (6)

8 Start, commencement (6)

10 Metallic cylinder used for storage (8)

11 Look at intently (5)

13 Rumour (7)

16 Atomic (7)

17 Having a sharp inclination (5)

20 Belonging to the past (8)

22 Take into custody (6)

24 Delivered a blow to (6)

25 In no specific place (8)

Down

1 Runs off to get married (6)

2 Animal kept as a domestic pet (3)

3 Drainage channel (5)

4 Showing signs of having had too much alcohol (7)

5 Metal food containers (4)

6 Produced by oneself, not mass manufactured (4-4)

9 Whorl (6)

12 People who travel for pleasure (8)

14 Somewhat (6)

15 Capsicum spice (7)

18 Tool used with a mortar (6)

19 Very frightening (5)

21 Tightly drawn (4)

23 Centre of a storm (3)

190

Across

1 Alfresco meals (7)

7 Grade of excellence (7)

8 Au revoir (5)

10 Abstract part of something (7)

11 Walk stealthily (5)

12 Law enforcement officer's vehicle (6,3)

16 Convertible, pliant (9)

18 Campaign period approaching an election (3-2)

20 Booth (7)

23 Compère (coll) (5)

24 Collective farm in Israel (7)

25 Diplomatic mission (7)

Down

1 Leaves of a book (5)

2 Personal magnetism (8)

3 High-pitched cry (6)

4 Crippled (4)

5 Presidential assistant (4)

6 Enigma (7)

9 Writing fluid receptacle (3-3)

13 Churchman (6)

14 Wife of an earl (8)

15 Scottish bread (7)

17 Light wind (6)

19 Political organisation (5)

21 Infant (4)

22 Most important point (4)

191

Across

1 Vehicles in motion (7)

5 Heavy wooden pole tossed as a test of strength (5)

7 Biting flies (5)

8 Become looser (7)

9 Interlace (7)

10 The first light of day (3-2)

11 Calm, with no emotional agitation (6)

13 In a slumber (6)

18 Kill by submerging in water (5)

20 Cut of meat (7)

21 Engage in a contest (7)

22 Bore a hole (5)

23 Birds' bills (5)

24 Brickwork (7)

Down

1 Female member of the cat family (7)

2 Item which enables something to be used in a way different from that for which it was intended (7)

3 Mode (7)

4 Kidney-shaped nut edible only when roasted (6)

5 Covers the surface of (5)

6 Put to death (7)

12 Fleshy pendulous part of the hearing organ (7)

14 Long steps (7)

15 Strong feeling (7)

16 Forfeit (7)

17 Hold in high regard (6)

19 Requires (5)

192

Across

1 Homicide without malice aforethought (12)

9 Toxic form of oxygen (5)

10 Protective garment (5)

11 Fish eggs (3)

12 Civilian clothing (5)

13 Abominate (7)

14 County of southern England (6)

16 Number of lines of verse (6)

20 Family appellation (7)

22 Venomous hooded snake (5)

24 Do something (3)

25 Ball-shaped (5)

26 Likeness (5)

27 Give a false or misleading account of the nature of (12)

Down

2 Detached (5)

3 Aseptic (7)

4 Agree (6)

5 Caprine animals (5)

6 Twisting of shape or position (7)

7 Gamut (5)

8 Universe (6)

15 Austrian composer of waltzes (7)

17 Strategy (7)

18 Proverbs (6)

19 Cup without a handle (6)

20 Firm open-weave fabric used by window-cleaners (5)

21 Mix up or confuse (5)

23 Organ enclosed within the skull (5)

193

Across

1 Gastrointestinal disorder (4,9)

7 Makes a wager (4)

8 Admirable quality or attribute (6)

9 Thin pancake (5)

10 Major monetary unit (4)

12 Approached (6)

13 Heathen (5)

15 Country of the Arabian Peninsula (5)

18 Encrustation that forms on the teeth and gums (6)

20 Salty Greek cheese (4)

21 Left-hand page (5)

22 Blanket-like cloak (6)

23 Unorthodox or false religion (4)

24 Making a positive impression on someone beforehand (13)

Down

1 Legendary (6)

2 Public dance hall (5)

3 Group of eight (5)

4 Three score and ten (7)

5 Meddle (9)

6 Avaricious (6)

11 Place in a different order (9)

14 Jittery (7)

16 Come to the fore (4,2)

17 Untidy, disorganised (6)

19 Bicker (5)

20 Concentrate (5)

194

Across

1 Native of La Paz, for example (8)

5 Supplication (4)

8 Fits of rage (8)

10 Church tower (7)

11 Daughter of a sibling (5)

12 Roman slave who led an uprising against Roman legions (9)

15 Doubt about someone's honesty (9)

18 Lost (2,3)

19 Move by degrees in one direction only (7)

22 Car exhaust (8)

23 Kill (4)

24 Moral excellence (8)

Down

1 Study of plants (6)

2 Portable lamps (8)

3 Subdivisions of a poem (6)

4 Weapons (4)

6 Spring up (4)

7 Admission (6)

9 Designating sound transmission from two sources (6)

13 Small padded envelope (6)

14 Engage in plotting (8)

15 Similar things placed in order (6)

16 Pinned down (6)

17 Animals used in desert regions (6)

20 Roman cloak (4)

21 Filled tortilla (4)

195

Across

1 Short underpants (6)
7 Milk pudding ingredient (7)
8 Spiny, insectivore with a long tongue and sharp claws (8)
9 Fail (to) (7)
10 All together, as a group (2,5)
13 Aquatic creature (5)
15 Poems (4)
16 Food used in a trap (4)
17 Extremely angry (5)
19 State of being behind in payments (7)
22 Psychics, supernaturalists (7)
24 Pursuit of pleasure as a matter of ethical principle (8)
25 Disc used in various board games (7)
26 Affirm by oath (6)

Down

2 Angry dispute (3-2)
3 Apartments (5)
4 Naked (4)
5 Very aggressive strain of insect (6,3)
6 Inflammation of the stomach lining (9)
7 Article of faith (5)
10 Branch of social science dealing with finance (9)
11 Helper (9)
12 Drink often mixed with alcohol (4)
14 Level (4)
18 Weapon that delivers a temporarily paralysing electric shock (5)
20 Fowl's perch (5)
21 Utters in an irritated tone (5)
23 Masticate (4)

196

Across

1 Deep red (7)
5 In the area (5)
8 Remark expressing careful consideration (11)
9 Souvenir (5)
11 Hard to catch (7)
13 Make numb (6)
14 Scribble (6)
17 Pearlescent (7)
18 Irritable, peevish (5)
19 Recklessly wasteful (11)
22 Branchlet (5)
23 Style, flair (7)

Down

1 Coalesced in soft thick lumps (7)
2 ___ and buts, objections (3)
3 Vast plain and National Park in Tanzania (9)
4 Straighten out (6)
5 Garland of flowers (3)
6 Person with whom one shares a secret (9)
7 Soup-serving spoon (5)
10 Australian arboreal marsupial (5,4)
12 Ambiguous (9)
15 Outfit (clothing and accessories) for a new baby (7)
16 Flee (6)
17 Desert watering-hole (5)
20 Duvet warmth rating (3)
21 The alphabet (inits) (3)

197

Across

1 Wrong in opinion or judgment (8)
6 Calls for (4)
9 Short sleep (3)
10 Battleground (5)
11 Country, capital Reykjavik (7)
12 Type of heron (5)
13 Mineral source (3,4)
15 Conjunction expressing a doubt or choice between alternatives (7)
17 Old-fashioned (7)
19 Desert, leave (7)
20 Italian poet (1265–1321) (5)
23 Heavenly body also known as Sirius (3,4)
24 Start abruptly (5)
25 Repent (3)
26 Spun thread (4)
27 Ignored, overlooked (6,2)

Down

1 Flesh (4)
2 Involuntary expulsion of air from the nose (6)
3 Savoury taste experience (4)
4 Social policy of racial segregation (9)
5 News chief (6)
7 Dishonoured (6)
8 Spare-time activity (8)
14 Hearers (9)
15 Exceptional creative ability (8)
16 Mick ___, English rock star associated with the Rolling Stones (6)
17 Girl's name (6)
18 Waited in line (6)
21 Factual (4)
22 Remain (4)

198

Across

1 Medicated lozenge for the throat (8)

5 Native of Glasgow, for example (4)

9 Fickle (7)

10 Mistake (5)

11 Synthetic (10)

14 Forest fire fighter (6)

15 Annoy continually (6)

17 Having special rights, advantages or immunities (10)

20 Imbecile (5)

21 Let up (4,3)

22 Consequently (4)

23 Arctic ruminants (8)

Down

1 Secret look (4)

2 Hindu woman's garment (4)

3 Around the middle of a scale of evaluation (12)

4 Acid found in milk (6)

6 Prominent bishop of the Roman Catholic Church (8)

7 With unflagging vitality (8)

8 Shop selling ready-to-eat food products (12)

12 Black lead (8)

13 Attractive and tempting (8)

16 Harsh, stern (6)

18 Hemispherical roof (4)

19 At a great distance (4)

199

Across

1 Rascal (5)

7 Enthusiastic approval (7)

9 Oil purification plant (8)

10 Slide unobtrusively (7)

12 Totalling (8)

14 Informal name for a cat (4)

16 Old-fashioned form of the word 'you' (4)

18 Game bird (8)

20 Putting words on paper (7)

23 Precious blue gemstone (8)

24 Brings to a final conclusion (7)

25 Ordered series (5)

Down

1 Military rank (8)

2 Be able to spare (6)

3 Section of glass (4)

4 Prevents (4)

5 Duck-billed creature (8)

6 Muscle that flexes the forearm (6)

8 Chamber within which a piston moves (8)

11 Dole out (medication) (8)

13 Individuality (8)

15 Scenery intended to stand alone (3,5)

17 Become set (6)

19 Heart condition marked by chest pain (6)

21 Strong sweeping cut made with a sharp instrument (4)

22 Musical composition (4)

200

Across

1 Receptacles for business documents (7,5)

9 Cowboy contest (5)

10 Primitive plant forms (5)

11 Speck (3)

12 Narrow backstreet (5)

13 Put into words (7)

14 Bunch of cords fastened at one end (6)

16 Relative position (6)

20 Sleeping room (7)

22 Largest artery of the body (5)

24 Adult male person (3)

25 Beauty parlour (5)

26 Figure out (5)

27 Meeting requirements (12)

Down

2 Relating to sea waves (5)

3 Analgesic (7)

4 Hurry (6)

5 Car wheel immobilising device (5)

6 Portion (7)

7 Stalks of a plant (5)

8 Bosom (6)

15 Blood-red (7)

17 Passage (7)

18 Formed (6)

19 Fleet of warships (6)

20 Prices (5)

21 Component parts of a skeleton (5)

23 Measuring stick (5)

201

Across

4 Localised sore (7)
8 Maxim (5)
9 Time between midday and evening (9)
10 Asian water lily (5)
11 Weedkiller (9)
13 Generator (6)
16 Internet photographic equipment (6)
20 Those who leave one country to settle in another (9)
23 Tablets (5)
24 Blasphemous behaviour (9)
25 Cloth woven from flax (5)
26 Greatest in size (7)

Down

1 Region of northern Europe (7)
2 Citadel (7)
3 Dog's lead (5)
4 People in a play (6)
5 Fawning in behaviour (7)
6 Species of bacteria which can threaten food safety (1,4)
7 Feel (5)
12 Chemical carrying genetic information (inits) (3)
14 Sweet potato (3)
15 Accumulation deposited by a glacier (7)
17 Rotating windstorm (7)
18 Absent (7)
19 To set in from a margin (6)
20 Artist's tripod (5)
21 Become liable to (5)
22 Incantation (5)

Solutions

1

A	L	P	A	C	A		E		F		L	
D		I			C	H	A	P	L	A	I	N
A	W	E	D		R		R		E		A	
M		D	E	P	I	C	T		E	U	R	O
S			L		D		H		T			B
A	B	B	E	Y		G	L	A	S	S	E	S
P			C		P		Y		T			T
P	E	P	T	A	L	K		A	R	G	U	E
L			A		A		G		E			T
E	M	I	T		C	A	R	T	E	L		R
	E		I		A		A		T	O	R	I
A	G	N	O	S	T	I	C			A		C
	A		N		E		E	X	O	D	U	S

2

	F		D		B		A	R	T	I	S	T
L	A	B	O	U	R	E	R		A		C	
	I		U		I		S	E	N	T	R	Y
C	R	I	B		B	S	E				A	
	E		L		E		N		A		P	
O	R	D	E	R		H	A	S	B	E	E	N
R			B		A		L		S			U
C	A	D	E	N	C	E		J	O	I	S	T
	C		D		Q		T		R		H	
	T				U	S	E		B	O	A	R
D	I	W	A	L	I		R		E		M	
	V		D		R	E	M	I	N	D	E	R
D	E	M	O	T	E		S		T		D	

3

P	A	C	E		A	U	D	A	C	I	T	Y
O		R		B		R		M		M		A
S	P	A	N	I	E	L		P	A	P	A	W
S		P		L				H		O		L
I	N	S	A	L	U	B	R	I	O	U	S	
B				I		U		T		N		B
L	O	G		A	L	L	A	H		D	U	O
E		U		R		G		E				N
	F	I	D	D	L	E	F	A	D	D	L	E
D		L		B				T		R		L
I	N	D	I	A		F	O	R	S	A	K	E
E		E		L		O		E		M		S
T	H	R	I	L	L	E	D		B	A	T	S

4

T	I	A	R	A		P	R	O	S	P	E	R
E		D		S	E	A		A		R		A
A	L	L	O	T		C		S	T	A	I	N
C		I		R		K		I		L		D
H		B	O	I	L	E	R	S	U	I	T	
I				D		T				N		N
N	I	C	K	E	L		C	H	E	E	S	E
G		A				B		A				E
	U	N	A	S	S	U	M	I	N	G		D
T		T		L		N		R		R		L
I	N	A	N	E		G		C	L	O	N	E
L		T		E		E	M	U		P		S
T	R	A	M	P	L	E		T	E	E	M	S

Solutions

5

P	U	M	I	C	E		S		C		P	
I		O			A	R	O	M	A	T	I	C
N	U	T	S		T		L		T		X	
G		H	A	B	E	R	D	A	S	H	E	R
P			L		N		I				L	
O	N	I	O	N		T	E	A	C	O	S	Y
N			N		I		R		L			E
G	O	D	S	E	N	D		C	O	C	O	A
	R				C		D		S			R
W	A	R	M	B	L	O	O	D	E	D		B
	C		A		I		M		T	I	T	O
A	L	L	I	A	N	C	E			R		O
	E		D		E		S	T	R	E	A	K

6

	G	L	O	V	E	P	U	P	P	E	T	S
D		I		I		O		O		D		C
O	P	A	L	S		S		O	L	I	V	E
L		R		C	U	E		L		F		N
L	A	S	S	O		R	E	S	P	I	T	E
O				U		S				C		
P	E	R	U	S	E		L	A	T	E	N	T
		E				A		T				E
L	I	P	R	E	A	D		T	U	B	E	R
I		L		L		D	I	E		O		R
L	O	I	R	E		U		M	A	N	G	O
A		C		M		C		P		E		R
C	L	A	R	I	N	E	T	T	I	S	T	

7

S	A	D	D	E	N		C		B			C
A		U		R		J	A	K	A	R	T	A
L	A	N	D	A	U		N		T			I
E		C			T	R	A	C	T	I	O	N
M	U	E	S	L	I		D		L		B	
	T		O		L	E	A	S	E		L	
B	O	A	T		I		G		C	R	A	B
	P		O	U	T	D	O		R		T	
	I		S		A		O	X	Y	G	E	N
C	A	R	P	A	R	K	S			R		O
A			E		I		E	S	C	O	R	T
P	Y	J	A	M	A	S		E		U		E
E			K		N		K	E	Y	P	A	D

8

H	E	I	N	O	U	S		C		S		B
A		M		K		C	O	R	O	L	L	A
N	I	A	G	A	R	A		I		I		R
G		G		P		M		M		N		R
E	L	I	C	I	T		L	E	A	G	U	E
R		N			E		O		C			L
	L	E	T	T	E	R	P	R	E	S	S	
C			E		T		E			A		G
A	T	T	A	C	H		D	R	O	W	S	E
R		I		L		F		U		M		Y
P		B		O		R	E	M	A	I	N	S
E	P	I	C	U	R	E		B		L		E
T		A		T		T	R	A	I	L	E	R

Solutions

9

I		D		F		C	O	N	T	A	C	T
T	H	E	I	R		O		A		B		I
A		C		A	E	R	O	P	L	A	N	E
L	A	I	T	Y		S		H		S		U
I		D		S	W	E	A	T	S	H	O	P
C		E				T		H			D	
S	A	D	I	S	M		T	A	M	P	E	R
	Y			U		C				R		E
C	E	L	E	B	R	A	T	E		E		T
L		I		L		B		M	U	F	T	I
A	B	O	R	I	G	I	N	E		E		R
S		N		M		N		N	E	R	V	E
P	O	S	S	E	S	S		D		S		D

10

F	R	A	N	T	I	C		S	T	O	N	E
I		G		U		A			I			X
R	I	G		N	O	R	M	A	L	I	S	E
E		R		G		B			T			R
B	R	A	Y	S		O			H	E	A	T
U		V		T	I	N	G	E		N		
G	L	A	D	E		D		Y	U	C	C	A
		T		N	A	I	V	E		O		C
C	R	E	W			O		S	L	U	S	H
U			H			X		I		R		I
B	E	H	E	A	D	I	N	G		A	X	E
I			R			D		H		G		V
C	R	I	E	D		E	X	T	R	E	M	E

11

E	N	M	I	T	Y		B	R	O	N	C	O
X		I		E		L		E		O		R
C	O	S	T	A	R	I	C	A		M		I
I		E		R		V		D	R	I	V	E
T	H	R	E	A	T	E	N			N		N
E				W		R		B		E	F	T
		P	E	A	T		D	A	T	E		
L	E	A		Y		Y		S				F
A		L			B	E	V	E	R	A	G	E
T	R	A	C	T		M		L		R		W
V		V		S	T	E	R	I	L	I	S	E
I		E		A		N		N		A		S
A	U	R	O	R	A		P	E	A	N	U	T

12

B	E	H	A	V	E		P	A	S	T	O	R
U		A		O			E			R		U
S	P	R	I	T	Z	E	R		L	A	W	N
T		D		E			P	R	O	P		S
A	B	S	U	R	D		L		A			
G		H			A	L	E	R	T	S		B
U	N	I	T		U		X		H	A	K	A
T		P	R	I	N	C	E			L		R
			A		T		D	Y	N	A	M	O
L		I	D	O	L			E		R		N
A	L	O	E		E	Q	U	A	L	I	S	E
T		W			S			R		E		S
E	R	A	S	E	S		A	S	I	D	E	S

Solutions

13

A	N	T	H	R	A	X		C	A	R	V	E
L		A		I				A		U		V
A		R		P		I	N	T	E	N	S	E
B	I	T	T	E	R	N		N		N		N
A		A		N		V		I		E	A	T
M	I	N	E	S	W	E	E	P	E	R		
A			V			R			Y			T
		D	E	L	I	N	Q	U	E	N	C	Y
U	S	E		A		E		G		I		C
N		T		B		S	H	A	M	P	O	O
Z	E	A	L	O	U	S		N		P		O
I		I		U				D		L		N
P	O	L	A	R		D	E	A	F	E	N	S

14

B	E	R	A	T	E		T	O	E	C	A	P
E		E		W		B		F		R		A
M	I	S	S	I	L	E		F	L	A	I	R
U		E		C		N	I	L		W		A
S	T	A	R	E		E		O				D
E		R				V		A	M	P	L	E
		C		A	V	O	I	D		O		
E	T	H	O	S		L				S		F
N				U		E		B	R	I	N	E
G		C		N	U	N		A		T		N
A	C	H	E	D		C	A	R	R	I	O	N
G		I		E		E		O		V		E
E	M	P	I	R	E		U	N	R	E	E	L

15

L	O	C	U	M		G	L	A	Z	I	E	R
E		U		I		R		D		N		E
A	R	R	A	N	G	E		D	A	V	I	D
S		T		U		A		T		E		F
H	E	A	R	T		S	P	O	U	S	A	L
		I		I		E				T		A
C	A	N	C	A	N		S	A	Y	I	N	G
U		R				D		B		G		
T	R	A	D	U	C	E		S	C	A	L	D
L		I		N		M		C		T		A
A	S	S	E	T		E	R	O	S	I	O	N
S		E		I		A		N		O		D
S	U	R	G	E	O	N		D	I	N	G	Y

16

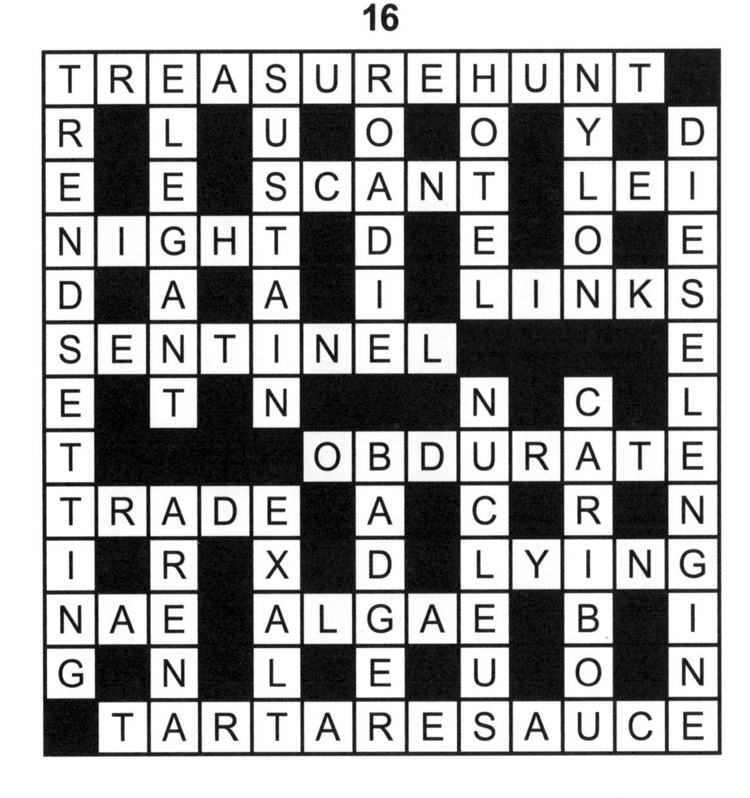

T	R	E	A	S	U	R	E	H	U	N	T	
R		L		U		O		O		Y		D
E		E		S	C	A	N	T		L	E	I
N	I	G	H	T		D		E		O		E
D		A		A		I		L	I	N	K	S
S	E	N	T	I	N	E	L					E
E		T		N				N		C		L
T					O	B	D	U	R	A	T	E
T	R	A	D	E		A		C		R		N
I		R		X		D		L	Y	I	N	G
N	A	E		A	L	G	A	E		B		I
G		N		L		E		U		O		N
	T	A	R	T	A	R	E	S	A	U	C	E

Solutions

17

P	E	D	I	C	A	B	■	I	■	A	S	S
■	D	■	■	R	■	E	N	D	O	N	■	H
F	U	L	F	I	L	S	■	E	■	D	■	O
■	C	■	■	M	■	I	N	S	T	A	N	T
C	A	R	R	I	E	D	■	■	■	N	■	P
■	T	■	■	N	■	E	■	D	■	T	■	U
C	E	R	E	A	L	■	D	I	G	E	S	T
O	■	E	■	L	■	V	■	N	■	■	E	■
M	■	L	■	■	■	E	M	O	T	I	V	E
P	L	A	S	T	E	R	■	S	■	■	E	■
A	■	P	■	I	■	S	E	A	B	I	R	D
S	■	S	A	D	H	U	■	U	■	■	A	■
S	H	E	■	E	■	S	T	R	O	L	L	S

18

O	C	C	U	P	A	N	T	■	T	A	L	L
C	■	R	■	R	■	E	■	W	■	B		E
T	R	A	D	E	R	S	■	R	A	D	O	N
O	■	M	■	P	■	T	■	I	■	O	■	D
P	O	S	T	A	G	E	S	T	A	M	P	S
U	■	■	■	R	■	D	■	E	■	E	■	■
S	O	B	B	E	D	■	I	R	O	N	I	C
■	■	R	■	D	■	A	■	S	■	■	■	A
D	R	A	I	N	I	N	G	B	O	A	R	D
A	■	V	■	E	■	S	■	L	■	L	■	E
C	O	A	T	S	■	W	O	O	L	L	E	N
H	■	D	■	S	■	E	■	C	■	O		Z
A	N	O	N	■	K	R	A	K	A	T	O	A

19

R	O	S	E	H	I	P	■	K	H	A	K	I
E	■	T	■	O	■	A	■	E	■	R	■	T
C	U	R	L	S	■	R	I	B	C	A	G	E
Y	■	I	■	T	■	L	■	A	■	B	■	M
C	A	P	R	I	C	E	■	B	A	S	I	S
L	■	E	■	L	■	Y	■	■	I	■	C	■
E	D	D	I	E	D	■	A	S	L	E	E	P
■	U	■	N	■	■	A	■	H	■	P	■	A
C	O	U	N	T	■	B	R	A	Z	I	E	R
L	■	D	■	H	■	U	■	L	■	S	■	A
E	N	D	L	E	S	S	■	L	O	T	U	S
A	■	E	■	M	■	E	■	O	■	L	■	O
N	U	R	S	E	■	R	A	W	D	E	A	L

20

R	A	S	C	A	L	■	P	E	D	A	L	O
A	■	■	H	■	E	■	E	■	■	B	■	P
C	H	R	I	S	T	M	A	S	T	R	E	E
E	■	A	■	■	■	O	■	W	■	A	■	R
■	■	N	■	C	A	R	D	I	A	C	■	E
D	A	K	A	R	■	T	■	F	■	A	C	T
A	■	A	■	I	D	I	O	T	■	D	■	T
Y	E	N	■	N	■	C	■	L	L	A	M	A
T	■	D	I	G	N	I	T	Y	■	B	■	■
O	■	F	■	E	■	A	■	■	■	R	■	A
D	R	I	B	S	A	N	D	D	R	A	B	S
A	■	L	■	■	D	■	U	■	A	■	■	K
Y	I	E	L	D	S	■	N	I	M	B	U	S

Solutions

21

S	T	A	Y	S		S	E	L	E	C	T	S
C		N		A		E		I		L		L
O	A	T		F	A	C	E	P	L	A	T	E
P		O		E		R				M		N
E	R	N	S	T		E	X	C	U	S	E	D
		Y		Y		T		H				E
A	D	M	I	N	I	S	T	R	A	T	O	R
S				E		E		Y		S		
C	H	A	P	T	E	R		S	L	A	P	S
E		S				V		A		R		E
T	R	I	E	N	N	I	A	L		I	R	A
I		D		A		C		I		N		R
C	L	E	A	N	S	E		S	C	A	B	S

22

B	A	Z	A	A	R		C		P		F	
O		I			I	C	E	C	R	E	A	M
R	I	N	D		D		N		O		S	
N		C	O	V	E	R	T		B	E	T	A
E			M		R		R		A		N	
O	C	T	E	T		E	A	R	T	H	E	N
	H		S		U		L		I		S	
D	I	S	T	A	N	T		C	O	P	S	E
	V		I		I		M		N			X
T	A	L	C		T	E	A	S	E	T		C
	L		A		I		K		R	A	G	E
P	R	E	T	E	N	C	E			C		E
	Y		E		G		R	I	O	T	E	D

23

	A	C	E	T	I	C		D	W	A	R	F
C		O		A		R		E		C		R
O	R	A	N	G	E	A	D	E		C		A
M		T				D		P	Y	L	O	N
P	L	I	M	S	O	L	L	S		A		K
O			A			E		E		I		I
S	Y	S	T	E	M		S	A	L	M	O	N
M		O		P		C			E			C
E		A		I	N	A	U	D	I	B	L	E
N	O	N	O	S		R				O		N
T		D		T	H	E	S	A	U	R	U	S
I		S		L		E		C		N		E
S	T	O	V	E		N	U	T	M	E	G	

24

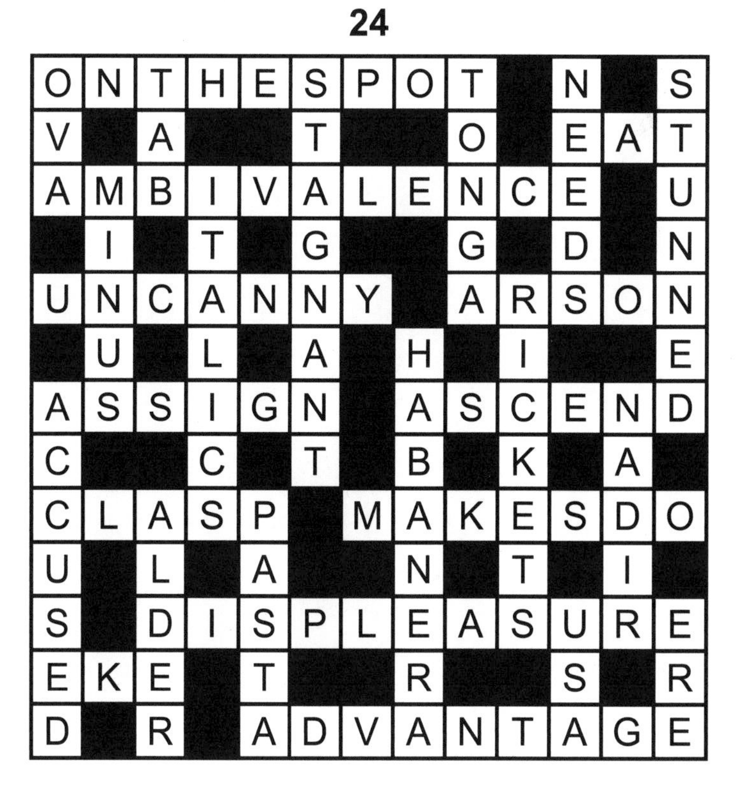

O	N	T	H	E	S	P	O	T		N		S
V		A			T			O		E	A	T
A	M	B	I	V	A	L	E	N	C	E		U
	I		T		G			G		D		N
U	N	C	A	N	N	Y		A	R	S	O	N
	U		L		A		H		I			E
A	S	S	I	G	N		A	S	C	E	N	D
C			C		T		B		K		A	
C	L	A	S	P		M	A	K	E	S	D	O
U		L		A			N		T		I	
S		D	I	S	P	L	E	A	S	U	R	E
E	K	E		T			R			S		R
D		R		A	D	V	A	N	T	A	G	E

Solutions

25

T	R	E	M	O	R		E		D		H	
A		P			E	X	A	M	I	N	E	R
C	R	I	B		A		R		E		R	
T		C	A	L	C	U	L	A	T	I	O	N
L			L		H		I				I	
E	A	G	L	E		R	E	F	L	E	C	T
S			O		R		R		E			A
S	C	A	T	T	E	R		C	A	M	E	L
	A				D		U		D			E
I	N	D	E	X	F	I	N	G	E	R		N
	C		P		L		C		R	A	F	T
D	E	M	E	R	A	R	A			C		E
	R		E		G		P	U	R	E	E	D

26

R	E	C	A	P			R		B	O	A	T
E		L		O	H	D	E	A	R		L	
P	R	O	M	S			S		I		K	
A		U		S	T	A	T	E	S	M	A	N
R	E	D		U			R		K		L	
T		Y		M	E	N	A	G	E	R	I	E
E			P		L		I		T			V
E	F	F	I	C	I	E	N	T		A		E
	O		T		G			A		C	A	R
G	R	E	E	T	I	N	G	S		T		Y
	M		O		B			T	R	I	A	D
	A		U	N	L	I	K	E		O		A
A	L	M	S		E			R	U	N	N	Y

27

C	A	T	A	C	O	M	B		D	E	E	D
O		O		U		A			A		D	
A	D	E	P	T		G	U	N	S	H	I	P
L		N		L	E	I			H		F	
G	U	A	V	A		C	A	L	O	R	I	E
A		I		S			L		F		C	
S	E	L	F	S	A	T	I	S	F	I	E	D
	Y		E		D			T		M		A
R	E	P	R	E	S	S		O	N	I	O	N
	H		V			E	A	R		T		G
C	O	V	E	R	U	P		A	B	A	S	E
	L		N			I		G		T		R
K	E	P	T		N	A	M	E	L	E	S	S

28

Solutions

29

B	R	O	U	G	H	T		A	S	P	I	C
O		B		O		E		C		A		A
T	R	I	A	L	A	N	D	E	R	R	O	R
H				D		U				T		V
E	M	C	E	E		R	E	S	P	I	R	E
R		H		N		E		H		T		
S	C	A	R	E	D		V	A	R	I	E	D
		I		Y		F		N		O		R
B	E	N	Z	E	N	E		G	E	N	I	E
A		M				N		R				S
T	R	A	F	F	I	C	L	I	G	H	T	S
C		I		A		E		L		O		E
H	I	L	L	Y		D	E	A	D	E	N	D

30

B	A	R	B		L	O	C	A	T	I	O	N
E		E		D		A		U		M		I
S	O	L	D	I	E	R		L	U	P	I	N
O		I		N				D		E		E
T	E	C	H	N	I	C	A	L	I	T	Y	
T				E		O		A		U		D
E	B	B		R	I	P	E	N		S	K	I
D		O		J		E		G				S
	I	N	C	A	N	D	E	S	C	E	N	T
A		F		C				Y		M		A
C	H	I	C	K		L	I	N	G	E	R	S
H		R		E		E		E		R		T
E	L	E	C	T	R	O	N		B	Y	T	E

31

C	R	U	M	P	E	T		B	E	A	R	D
U		S		R		H	A	S		M		E
B	E	E	L	I	N	E		E	X	P	E	L
I				V		I				H		A
C	A	C	T	I		S	U	B	S	I	D	Y
L		H		L		M		R		B		
E	D	I	T	E	D		P	O	L	I	S	H
		P		G		W		A		A		A
C	H	O	L	E	R	A		D	I	N	A	R
O		L				L		C				N
S	C	A	N	T		L	E	A	K	A	G	E
T		T		O	D	E		S		W		S
S	H	A	D	E		T	E	T	A	N	U	S

32

R	A	T	I	O		S	A	L	U	T	E	S
O		H		B	O	O		E		O		P
S	P	U	D	S		L		A	O	R	T	A
E		G		C		E		R		M		M
M	A	S	T	E	R	M	I	N	D	E	D	
A				N		N				N		B
R	O	T	T	E	N		T	S	E	T	S	E
Y		H				O		E				L
	D	I	S	C	O	U	R	A	G	I	N	G
B		N		O		T		N		M		I
A	N	N	U	M		L		C	O	P	R	A
G		E		M		A	X	E		E		N
S	T	R	E	A	K	Y		S	E	L	L	S

Solutions

33

34

D	A	M	E	■	L	A	Y	A	B	O	U	T
E	■	U	■	T	■	C	■	R	■	C		I
C	O	M	P	E	E	R	■	C	H	A	I	R
I	■	P	■	R	■	O	■	H	■	R		E
B	A	S	I	C	■	S	P	I	R	I	T	S
E	■	■	■	E	■	S	■	T	■	N	■	■
L	E	G	E	N	D	■	D	E	M	A	N	D
■	■	A	■	T	■	S	■	C	■	■	■	R
E	A	R	N	E	S	T	■	T	I	A	R	A
R	■	D	■	N	■	A	■	U	■	L		W
O	P	E	R	A	■	V	E	R	B	O	S	E
D	■	N	■	R	■	E	■	E	■	H		R
E	S	S	A	Y	I	S	T	■	B	A	R	S

35

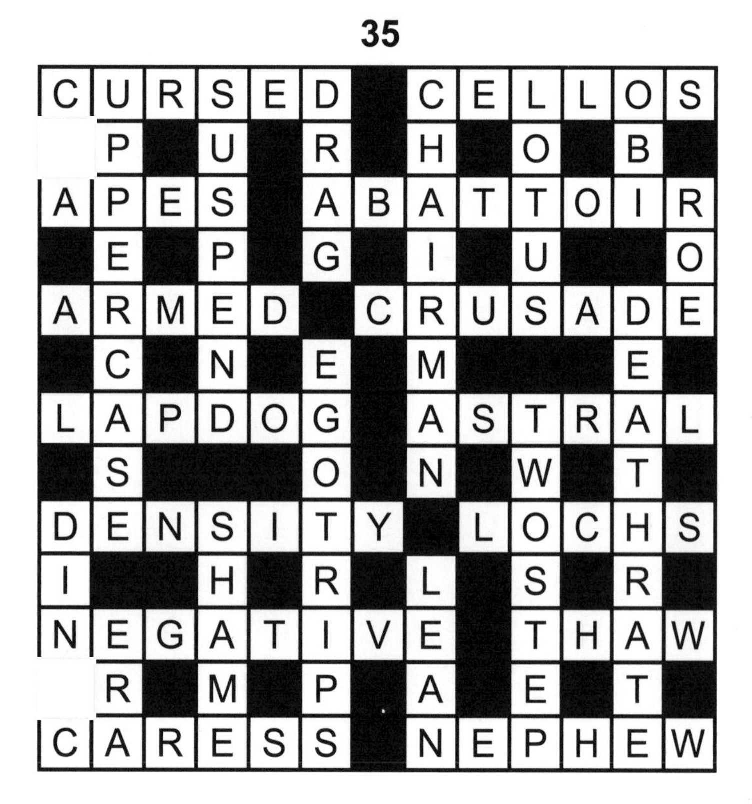

36

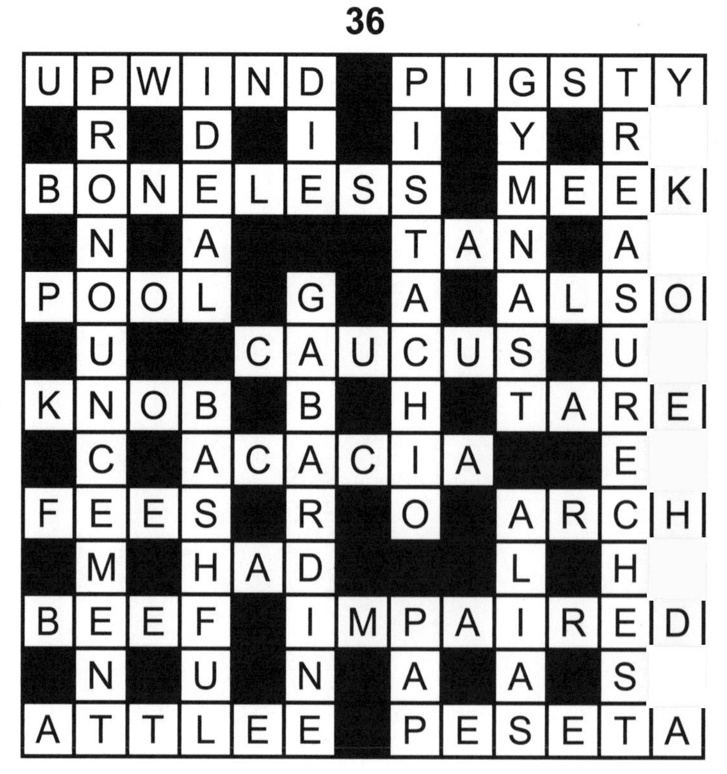

Solutions

37

S	A	I	D		S	P	E	C	I	M	E	N
U		T		C		H		A		A		E
F	L	A	V	O	U	R		T	A	R	T	S
F		L		N		A		E		R		T
E	G	Y	P	T		S	T	R	A	I	N	
R				I		E		P		E		P
E	X	P	A	N	D		W	I	L	D	E	R
D		R		U		P		L				O
	B	E	C	O	M	E		L	Y	I	N	G
B		P		U		R		A		M		R
A	R	A	B	S		S	U	R	N	A	M	E
K		R		L		O		S		G		S
E	V	E	R	Y	O	N	E		B	E	D	S

38

C	L	A	S	S	I	C	A	L		C	A	T
A		P		H		R		O		H		I
N	A	O	M	I		O		G	R	A	T	E
C		L		A	S	S		I		L		R
A	L	L	O	T		S	E	C	R	E	T	E
N		O		S		Q				T		D
			B	U	R	U	N	D	I			
C		F				E		I		C		R
A	M	O	R	O	U	S		S	H	A	K	E
S		R		P		T	E	A		N		C
I	D	I	O	T		I		B	R	O	K	E
N		N		I		O		L		E		S
G	E	T		C	O	N	S	E	N	S	U	S

39

N	A	U	S	E	A		D		F			B
	B		U		S	N	O	W	L	I	N	E
A	I	S	L	E	S		Z		O			T
	D		K		E	L	E	V	A	T	O	R
V	E	R	S	U	S				T			O
O		U			S	H	A	P	E	D		T
L	A	S	T		O		R		R	A	S	H
U		H	E	A	R	E	R			D		E
N			N				O	X	F	O	R	D
T	R	U	D	G	I	N	G		A		A	
A			R		R		A	C	C	E	N	T
R	E	L	I	G	I	O	N		E		C	
Y			L		S		T	E	T	C	H	Y

40

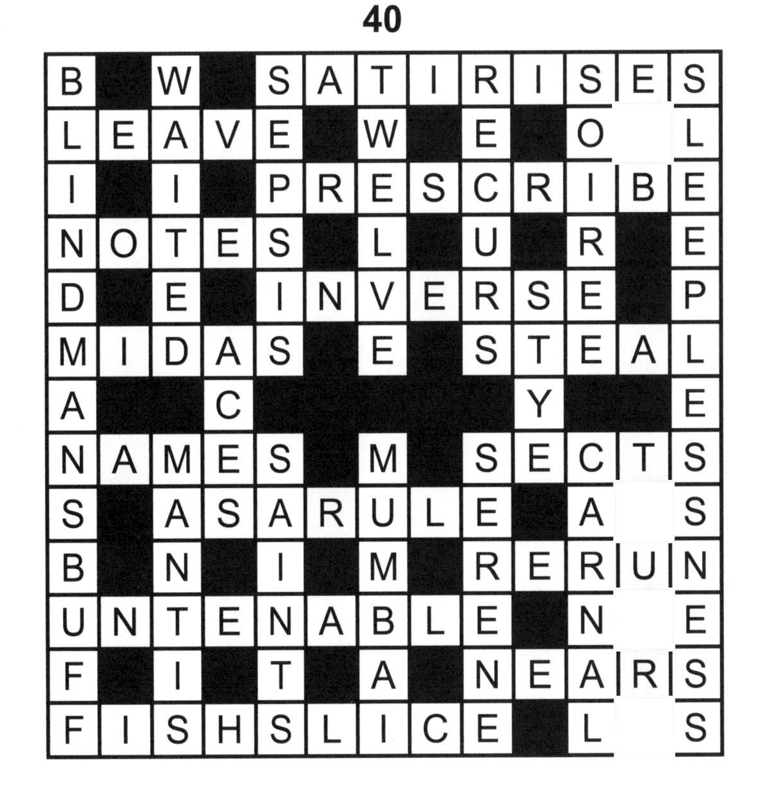

Solutions

41

S	E	N	D	S		L			P			L
E		U		Y		E	U	R	A	S	I	A
A	I	M		L		E			N			S
L		B		V	E	R	S	A	T	I	L	E
O	P	E	R	A			C		H			R
F		R		N	A	P	O	L	E	O	N	
F			C		V		N		R			A
	I	M	A	G	I	N	E	S		F		C
A			N		A			E	R	R	O	R
B	Y	S	T	A	N	D	E	R		E		E
Y			E			E		M		S	E	A
S	O	M	E	O	N	E		O		C		G
M			N			D		N	O	O	S	E

42

N	O	S	Y		T	U	N	E	L	E	S	S
A		T		K		N		M		V		E
T	U	R	K	I	S	H		B	R	A	W	L
I		A		N		O		A		S		F
V	O	W	E	D		L	O	R	R	I	E	S
I				E		Y		R		O		A
T	U	T	O	R	S		C	A	N	N	O	T
Y		U		G		H		S				I
P	A	R	T	A	K	E		S	E	E	P	S
L		M		R		C		I		L		F
A	F	O	O	T		K	O	N	T	I	K	I
Y		I		E		L		G		D		E
S	I	L	E	N	C	E	R		R	E	A	D

43

C	A	R	E	R		M	A	H	A	T	M	A
A		E		E		A		A		R		R
I	M	P		M	I	N	E	S	H	A	F	T
R		R		A		I				C		I
N	A	O	M	I		F	A	W	N	E	R	S
		O		N		E		A				T
L	I	F	E	I	N	S	U	R	A	N	C	E
E				N		T		M		E		
A	N	T	I	G	U	A		O	L	I	V	E
R		R				T		N		T		X
N	E	A	R	T	H	I	N	G		H	I	P
E		P		I		O		E		E		E
D	I	S	C	E	R	N		R	U	R	A	L

44

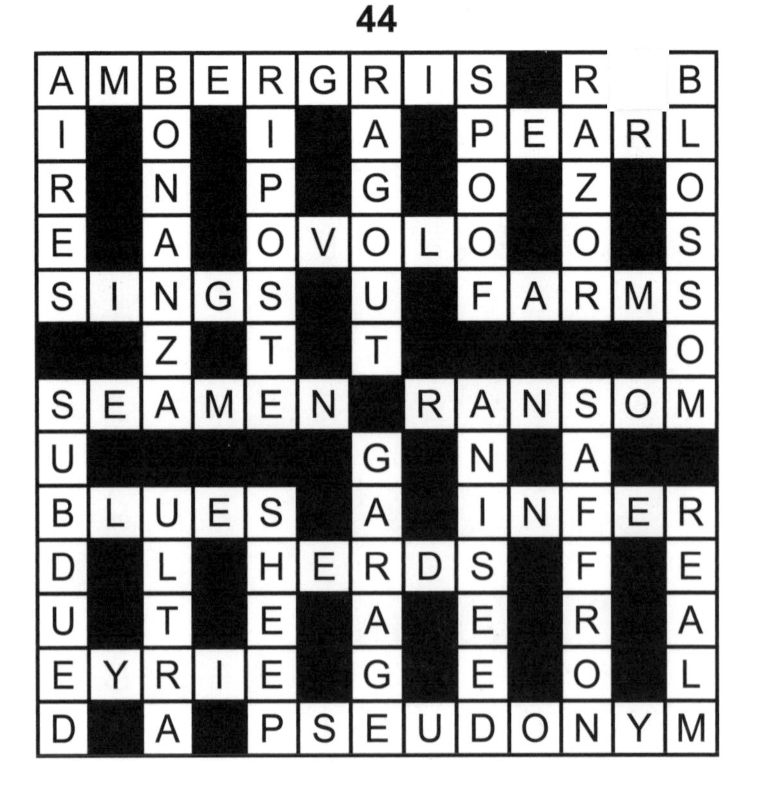

A	M	B	E	R	G	R	I	S		R		B
I		O		I		A		P	E	A	R	L
R		N		P		G		O		Z		O
E		A		O	V	O	L	O		O		S
S	I	N	G	S		U		F	A	R	M	S
		Z		T		T						O
S	E	A	M	E	N		R	A	N	S	O	M
U						G		N		A		
B	L	U	E	S		A		I	N	F	E	R
D		L		H	E	R	D	S		F		E
U		T		E		A		E		R		A
E	Y	R	I	E		G		E		O		L
D		A		P	S	E	U	D	O	N	Y	M

Solutions

45

S	A	L	A	A	M		O		C		L	
T		E			A	P	P	R	O	V	A	L
A	S	S			R		E		M		T	
V		S	H	A	R	O	N		P	A	T	E
E		O			Y		A		U		E	
S	E	R	G	E		C	I	S	T	E	R	N
			U		D		R		E			
A	S	H	A	M	E	D		B	R	A	S	S
	E		R		B		T			S		E
L	A	I	D		A	C	R	O	S	S		P
	L		I		T		I			U	L	T
D	E	C	A	D	E	N	T			M		E
	D		N		D		E	X	C	E	P	T

46

P	A	S	S	O	U	T		B		H		F
A		T		A		I	R	O	N	A	G	E
L	I	A	I	S	O	N		M		U		E
L		P		I		S		B		N		L
E	N	L	I	S	T		S	E	T	T	L	E
T		E			U		L					R
	G	R	A	N	D	F	A	T	H	E	R	
L					O		B			D		Z
A	P	P	E	A	R		S	Q	U	I	R	E
R		R		B		M		U		T		P
Y		O		B		A	B	O	L	I	S	H
N	E	W	Y	E	A	R		T		O		Y
X		L		Y		C	L	E	A	N	E	R

47

S		L		R		P	O	S	T	M	A	N
P	L	A	T	E	A	U				E		I
I		B		P		R		S	L	A	I	N
T	H	E	M	E		S	R	I		D		E
		L		T		U		S	C	O	O	P
P	E	S	T	I	L	E	N	T		W		I
H				T				E				N
A		S		I	G	N	O	R	A	M	U	S
R	A	T	I	O		U		I		E		
I		R		U	S	A		N	Y	M	P	H
S	L	A	M	S		N		L		O		I
E		N				C	O	A	X	I	N	G
E	N	D	G	A	M	E		W		R		H

48

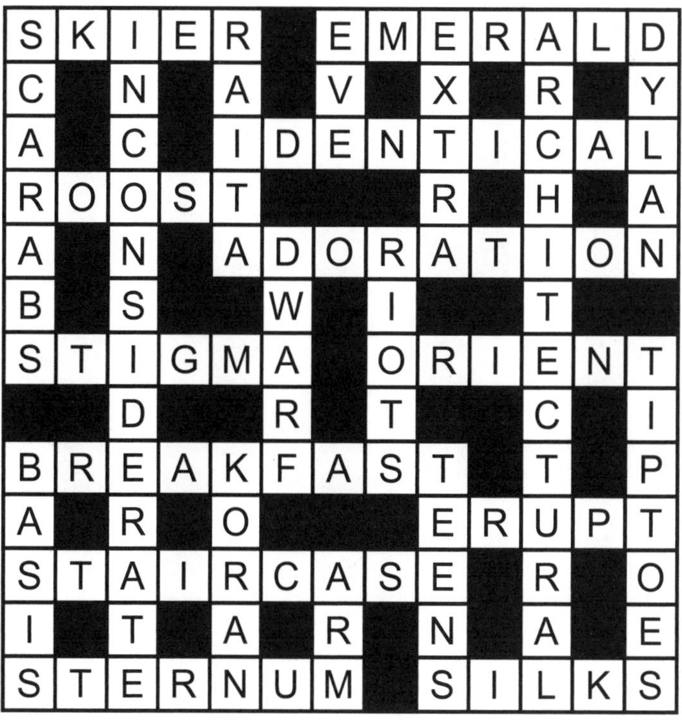

S	K	I	E	R		E	M	E	R	A	L	D
C		N		A		V		X		R		Y
A		C		I	D	E	N	T	I	C	A	L
R	O	O	S	T				R		H		A
A		N		A	D	O	R	A	T	I	O	N
B		S			W		I			T		
S	T	I	G	M	A		O	R	I	E	N	T
		D			R		T			C		I
B	R	E	A	K	F	A	S	T		T		P
A		R		O				E	R	U	P	T
S	T	A	I	R	C	A	S	E		R		O
I		T		A		R		N		A		E
S	T	E	R	N	U	M		S	I	L	K	S

Solutions

49

M	I	N	D	S	E	T		H		D		M
O		E		A			C	I	C	A	D	A
N		E		L		E		P		V		K
A	R	D	U	O	U	S		S	P	I	N	E
R		F		N		T		T		D		R
C	R	U	X		B	A	G	E	L			
H		L		J		B		R		V		T
			Q	U	E	L	L		H	I	D	E
S		P		N		I		B		O		S
O	M	A	N	I		S	H	A	L	L	O	T
U		N		P		H		C		A		I
T	E	E	T	E	R			K		T		F
H		L		R		F	I	S	H	E	R	Y

50

B	A	S	E	B	A	L	L		P	A	I	D
U		T		O		O			E			E
F		O		R		O	R	G	A	N	I	C
F	O	R	C	E	P	S			C			L
		E				E	S	T	O	N	I	A
C	A	S	E	M	E	N	T		C			R
R			T		L		A		K			E
O			E		S	T	R	E	S	S	E	D
S	M	A	R	T	E	R				K		
S			N			A	T	T	R	A	C	T
C	A	R	I	B	O	U		U		T		R
U			T			M		F		E		O
T	I	N	Y		D	A	Y	T	O	D	A	Y

51

C	I	R	R	U	S		M		A		R	
A		E			E	X	A	M	I	N	E	R
M	E	G			T		T		R		V	
P		I	N	D	I	C	T		S	P	A	N
U		O			N		H		P		M	
S	U	N	N	Y		R	E	C	E	I	P	T
			I		B		W		E			
B	A	T	T	E	R	Y		A	D	M	I	T
	M		R		I		W			U		R
C	O	C	O		S	C	A	L	D	S		O
	U		G		K		S			T	O	P
I	N	T	E	R	E	S	T			E		H
	T		N		T		E	N	E	R	G	Y

52

Solutions

53

B	I	T	E		T	R	A	I	N	S	E	T
A		W		C		U		N		H		W
C	Y	A	N	I	D	E		E	V	A	D	E
K		I		V				X		V		E
L	A	N	D	I	N	G	S	T	R	I	P	
A				L		L		R		N		B
S	I	P		S	W	A	M	I		G	O	A
H		R		E		D		C				R
	P	O	O	R	R	E	L	A	T	I	O	N
A		W		V				B		A		A
D	E	L	T	A		I	S	L	A	M	I	C
D		E		N		K		E		B		L
S	P	R	I	T	Z	E	R		B	I	L	E

54

D	E	J	A	V	U		D		M		D	
	L		R		P	R	O	M	O	T	E	R
D	E	P	I	C	T		G		O		F	
	C		S		O	B	S	E	R	V	E	R
A	T	T	E	N	D				I		R	
B					A	R	S	O	N	I	S	T
L			R		T		U		G			A
E	N	D	U	S	E	R	S					I
	A		S				P	O	S	T	A	L
D	I	S	T	A	S	T	E		M		L	
	L		I		T		N	I	A	C	I	N
R	E	D	C	R	O	S	S		R		E	
	D		S		W		E	X	T	E	N	T

55

S	E	R	V	I	C	E		B		H		T
L		A		N			B	O	T	A	N	Y
I		D		K		A		O		Z		P
T	R	I	C	E	P	S		S	I	E	V	E
H		C		D		S		T		L		S
E	L	A	N		L	A	Y	E	R			
R		L		C		I		R		C		P
			M	A	N	L	Y		H	A	L	O
S		B		R		A		U		D		R
H	Y	E	N	A		N	A	S	C	E	N	T
O		L		V		T		U		N		E
R	A	T	T	A	N			R		C		N
E		S		N		P	A	Y	M	E	N	T

56

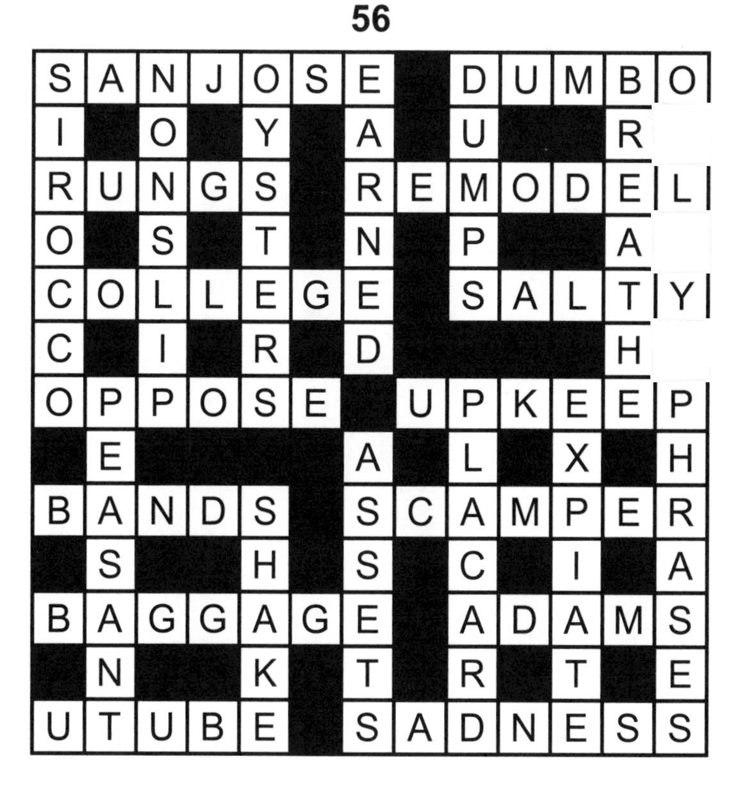

S	A	N	J	O	S	E		D	U	M	B	O
I		O		Y		A		U			R	
R	U	N	G	S		R	E	M	O	D	E	L
O		S		T		N		P			A	
C	O	L	L	E	G	E		S	A	L	T	Y
C		I		R		D					H	
O	P	P	O	S	E		U	P	K	E	E	P
	E					A		L		X		H
B	A	N	D	S		S	C	A	M	P	E	R
	S			H		S		C		I		A
B	A	G	G	A	G	E		A	D	A	M	S
	N			K		T		R		T		E
U	T	U	B	E		S	A	D	N	E	S	S

Solutions

57

58

59

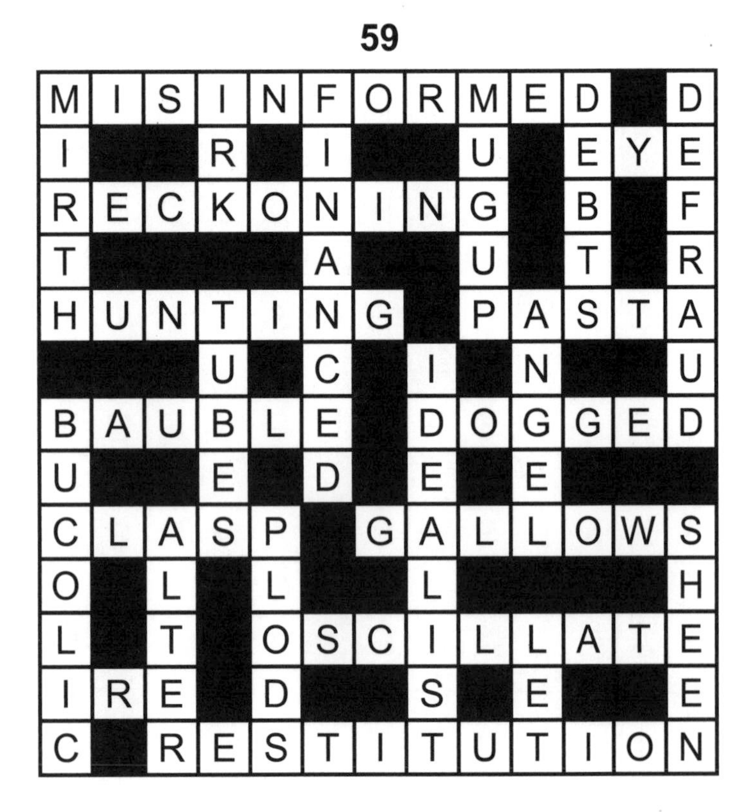

60

Solutions

61

S	U	L	K	S		L			B			M
K		I		U		E	X	C	R	E	T	E
I	F	S		R		G			E			T
P		T		R	I	O	G	R	A	N	D	E
P	I	E	C	E			E		K			R
E		D		Y	O	U	N	G	E	S	T	
R			C		U		R		R			O
	S	H	A	N	T	I	E	S		V		D
H			R		E			L	O	U	S	Y
E	X	O	N	E	R	A	T	E		L		S
A			A			R		U		G	A	S
R	I	N	G	L	E	T		T		A		E
D			E			Y		H	A	R	R	Y

62

H	E	C	T	I	C		F	I	S	C	A	L
	M		R		E		E		C			E
R	O	T	U	N	D		S	E	A	N	C	E
	T		S		A	C	T		N			K
F	I	L	T	E	R		O		D		P	
	O					D	O	W	A	G	E	R
	N		M		W		N		L		R	
P	A	T	R	I	O	T					P	
	L		R		U		A	D	D	L	E	D
A			I		N	I	B		E		T	
R	A	G	G	E	D		B	U	N	K	U	M
C			H		E		O		I		A	
H	I	N	T	E	D		T	E	M	P	L	E

63

B	L	I	N	D		D	I	S	U	S	E	D
L		S		E		O		A		H		I
O	P	T		S	Q	U	A	D	C	A	R	S
N		H		E		B				W		O
D	E	M	U	R		L	A	I	D	L	O	W
		U		T		E		N				N
C	A	S	H	R	E	G	I	S	T	E	R	S
O				A		L		U		N		
N	A	P	H	T	H	A		R	O	M	E	O
C		E				Z		G		A		I
E	X	T	R	A	D	I	T	E		S	O	L
D		E		I		N		N		S		E
E	A	R	P	L	U	G		T	W	E	E	D

64

M	I	M	I	C		A	R	S	E	N	I	C
O		E		H		D		E		A		O
A	N	D	R	O	I	D		E	Q	U	A	L
T		I		O		U		D		T		O
S	A	T	E	S		C	A	S	T	I	N	G
		E		E		E				C		N
B	A	R	E	S	T		O	C	T	A	V	E
E		R				E		O		L		
S	T	A	R	R	E	D		M	U	M	P	S
I		N		H		G		M		I		T
D	I	E	G	O		I	D	E	A	L	L	Y
E		A		M		N		N		E		L
S	A	N	D	B	A	G		T	A	S	T	E

Solutions

65

S	Y	M	P	A	T	H	Y		F	R	E	E
H		A		C		O		M		E		R
A	I	T	C	H		S	N	A	F	F	L	E
P				I		T		T		L		C
I		S	E	L	F	E	V	I	D	E	N	T
N		H		L		L		N		X		
G	A	R	D	E	N		P	E	R	I	O	D
		I		S		P		E		V		A
S	Y	N	C	H	R	O	N	I	S	E		Z
E		K		E		R		D				Z
D	I	A	L	E	C	T		O	F	F	A	L
G		G		L		I		L		R		E
E	Y	E	S		P	A	S	S	W	O	R	D

66

T	I	M	E	D		A	B	S	E	N	C	E
I		I		E		L		T		E		A
M	U	S	I	C	A	L		A	G	I	N	G
I		C		I		O		R		G		E
D	R	E	A	M		W	H	E	T	H	E	R
		L		A		S				B		L
B	O	L	D	L	Y		M	E	M	O	R	Y
I		A				A		S		U		
C	A	N	D	L	E	S		C	U	R	V	E
Y		E		O		P		A		H		N
C	H	O	R	D		E	X	P	L	O	R	E
L		U		G		C		E		O		M
E	A	S	I	E	S	T		D	A	D	D	Y

67

	N	O	N	C	O	M	B	A	T	A	N	T
R		O		Y		A		B		P		U
U	N	Z	I	P		G		I	M	P	E	L
S		E		R	U	N		D		O		L
S	I	D	L	E		E	R	E	M	I	T	E
I				S		T				N		
A	R	R	E	S	T		N	A	N	T	E	S
		I				D		B				T
D	I	C	T	A	T	E		S	E	V	E	R
R		K		G		B	I	T		I		E
O	M	E	G	A		R		A	D	O	R	E
N		T		V		I		I		L		T
E	A	S	T	E	R	S	U	N	D	A	Y	

68

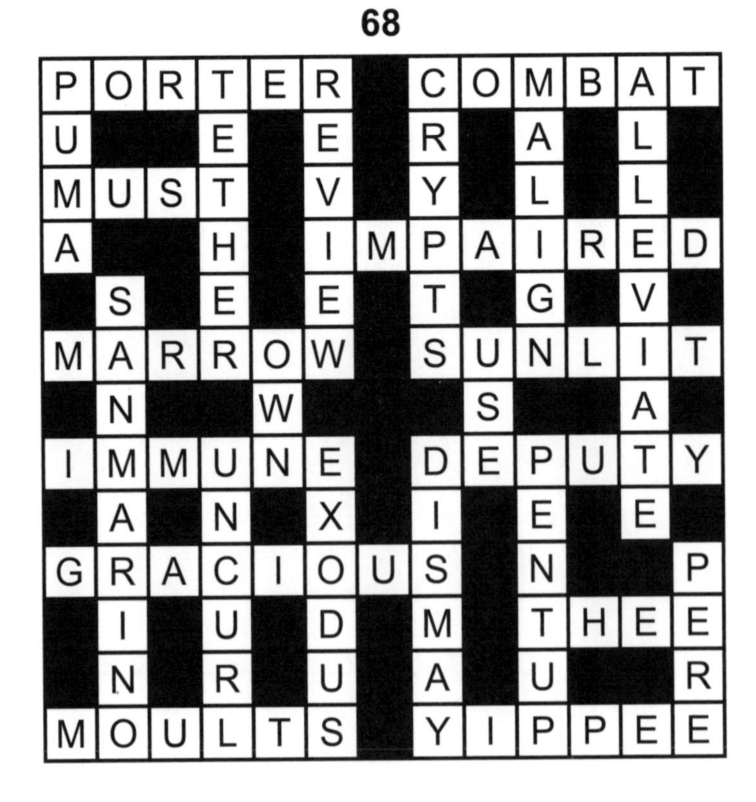

P	O	R	T	E	R		C	O	M	B	A	T
U			E		E		R		A		L	
M	U	S	T		V		Y		L		L	
A			H		I	M	P	A	I	R	E	D
	S		E		E		T		G		V	
M	A	R	R	O	W		S	U	N	L	I	T
	N			W				S			A	
I	M	M	U	N	E		D	E	P	U	T	Y
	A		N		X		I		E		E	
G	R	A	C	I	O	U	S		N			P
	I		U		D		M		T	H	E	E
	N		R		U		A		U			R
M	O	U	L	T	S		Y	I	P	P	E	E

Solutions

69

A	T	O	M	I	C		F		C			P
	H			R		C	A	R	O	U	S	E
A	E	R	I	A	L		I		S			N
	T			T		P	R	E	T	E	N	D
C	A	N	C	E	L				A			U
R			E		I	N	C	U	R			L
A	N	T	S		A		A		I	N	F	O
F			S	T	R	U	T		C			U
T			A				S	M	A	R	T	S
S	M	O	T	H	E	R		O			A	
M			I		S		A	C	C	R	U	E
A	C	R	O	B	A	T		H			P	
N			N		U		C	A	M	B	E	R

70

C	R	O	T	C	H	E	T		M	A	S	T
H		T		R		N				M		A
A	G	I	L	E		D	I	S	C	U	S	S
P		T		S		E				L		T
		I		C		A	C	A	D	E	M	E
M	I	S	H	E	A	R		C		T		B
A				N				T				U
R		A		D		U	N	S	O	U	N	D
S	E	N	I	O	R	S		O		N		
H		G				E		F		E		T
G	L	I	S	T	E	N		G	U	S	T	O
A		N				E		O		C		P
S	P	A	T		S	T	U	D	I	O	U	S

71

C	O	A	T	S			U		S	I	C	K
H		P		T	R	A	N	C	E		H	
A	L	P	H	A			S		T		I	
T		E		T	H	R	E	E	S	O	M	E
T	U	N		I			T		A		N	
Y		D		C	O	N	T	A	I	N	E	R
	M		T		R		L		L		Y	
R	A	M	R	A	I	D	E	R		V		R
	D		I		G			E		E	T	A
R	E	A	C	T	I	O	N	S		R		R
	I		K		N			O	N	I	C	E
	R		L	E	A	D	E	R		T		S
F	A	K	E		L			T	R	Y	S	T

72

S	O	A	R		N	A	R	C	O	T	I	C
E		T		P		R		R		R		A
A	I	L	E	R	O	N		O	S	I	E	R
W		A		I		I		S		P		S
A	R	S	O	N		C	A	S	T	L	E	
T				C		A		C		E		R
E	S	C	H	E	W		B	O	W	T	I	E
R		H		R		C		U				P
	C	A	R	E	E	R		N	A	D	I	R
C		P		G		A		T		I		I
A	W	A	R	E		F	O	R	S	A	K	E
P		T		N		T		Y		N		V
S	K	I	T	T	I	S	H		D	A	R	E

Solutions

73

S	T	I	F	F	E	S	T		D	A	M	S
T		N		O		W				U		O
A	B	N	O	R	M	A	L			T		L
R		O		M		P	E	R	G	O	L	A
V	I	C	T	I	M		A					C
E		E		C	A	R	T	H	O	R	S	E
		N			L		H			E		
O	U	T	N	U	M	B	E	R		N		G
N					S		R	E	P	E	A	L
H	A	T	C	H	E	T		M		G		O
O		A			Y	O	K	O	H	A	M	A
L		C				A		V		D		T
D	U	T	Y		I	D	L	E	N	E	S	S

74

	H	A	P	P	Y	G	O	L	U	C	K	Y
G		N		O		A		I		A		A
Y	I	K	E	S		N		L	Y	R	I	C
P		L		S	O	D		A		W		H
S	C	E	N	E		E	N	C	H	A	N	T
U				S		R				S		
M	O	R	O	S	E		N	A	C	H	O	S
		E				B		S				I
S	I	S	T	I	N	E		S	E	R	U	M
T		P		R		L	E	U		U		I
A	M	I	G	O		U		R	E	N	A	L
F		R		N		G		E		I		E
F	R	E	E	S	T	A	N	D	I	N	G	

75

S	A	L	L	O	W		C		U		C	
O		A			A	G	R	A	R	I	A	N
R		T			T		Y		E		R	
B	E	H	A	V	E		S	W	A	Y	E	D
E			N		R		T				L	
T	A	N	G	O		C	A	N	D	I	E	D
	R		S		G		L		O		S	
P	O	T	T	E	R	Y		S	W	I	S	S
	M				A		P		N			A
R	A	I	S	I	N		R	O	S	A	R	Y
	T		U		T		U			N		I
D	I	V	I	D	E	N	D			T		N
	C		T		D		E	Y	E	I	N	G

76

S	P	A	R	T	A	C	U	S		B		B
A		U		W		A		W	H	A	L	E
L	A	D		I		M		E		C		A
E		I		S	U	E	D	E		O		V
M	O	T	E	T		R		T	E	N	S	E
		O		E		A						R
S	T	R	I	D	E		S	L	A	C	K	S
U						C		O		L		
F	O	C	U	S		A		B	R	A	T	S
F		O		T	O	N	N	E		P		O
I		W		A		N		L		P	I	N
C	H	E	F	S		E		I		E		N
E		R		H	U	S	B	A	N	D	R	Y

Solutions

77

R	U	S	T	I	C		R	A	S	C	A	L
	P		E		H		O		T		V	
S	P	O	T		E	D	U	C	A	T	E	D
	E		A		W		L		T			
T	R	E	N	D		G	E	N	E	R	I	C
	C		U		I		T				N	
B	A	L	S	A	M		T	R	O	U	G	H
	S				B		E		L		E	
L	E	V	E	R	E	T		F	I	E	N	D
			X		C		K		V		U	
C	A	L	A	M	I	N	E		I	C	O	N
	I		L		L		L		E		U	
W	R	I	T	H	E		P	U	R	I	S	T

78

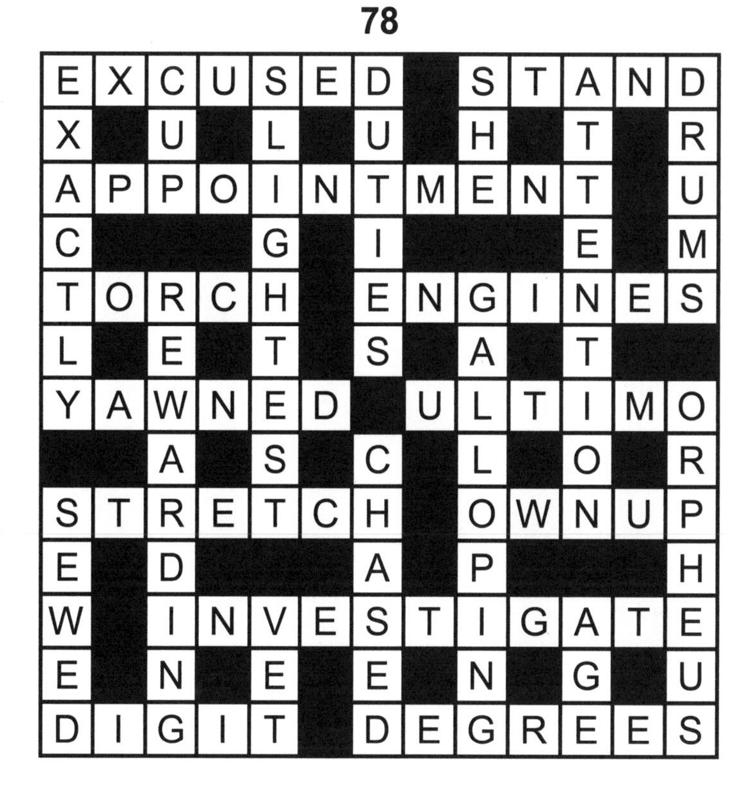

79

I	C	E	B	E	R	G		N		G	A	B
	H			Y		U	V	U	L	A		E
A	I	M	L	E	S	S		T		Z		E
	M			L		S		S	W	E	A	T
D	E	P	R	I	V	E	D			L		L
	R			N		T		E		L		E
C	A	C	H	E	T		E	G	R	E	S	S
O		L		R		C		G			A	
N		E			S	H	O	W	G	I	R	L
G	R	A	S	S		R		H			D	
E		N		O		I	D	I	O	T	I	C
S		S	C	A	M	S		T			N	
T	H	E		P		T	R	E	A	T	E	D

80

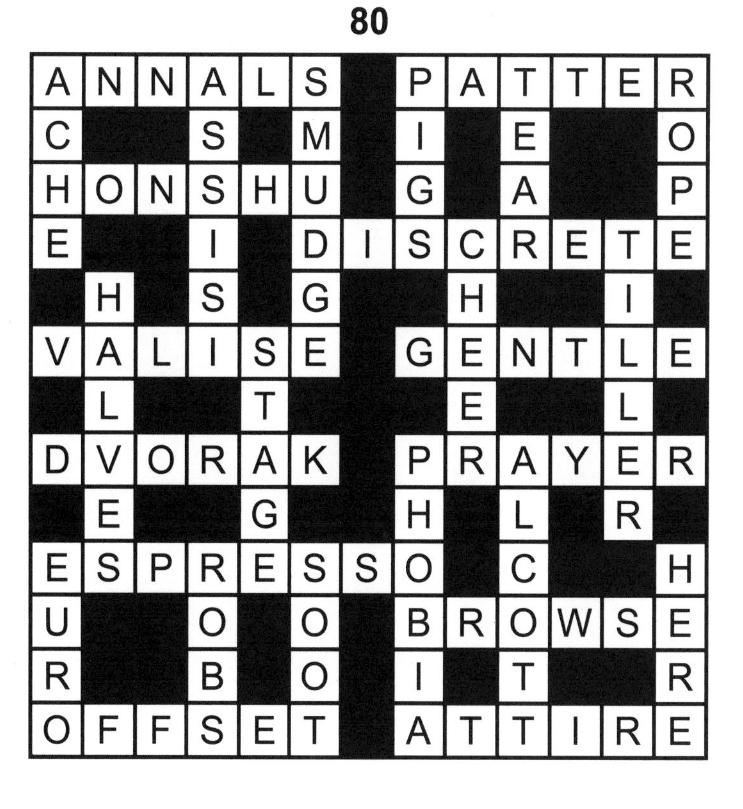

Solutions

81

82

U	P	S	H	O	T		S	E	T	O	U	T
	R		A		E		E		R		R	
C	O	N	S		A	C	A	D	E	M	I	C
	S		S		M		H		N			
V	E	N	O	M		L	O	U	D	E	S	T
	C		C		C		R				N	
C	U	C	K	O	O		S	O	C	I	A	L
	T				H		E		H		K	
L	E	A	R	N	E	R		F	A	M	E	D
			A		S		W		N		B	
R	O	A	D	S	I	D	E		N	A	I	L
	D		A		O		E		E		T	
N	E	U	R	O	N		P	E	L	L	E	T

83

84

Solutions

85

C	H	A	I	N	S	M	O	K	E	R		S
A			L		T			I		A	N	Y
R	O	C	K	N	R	O	L	L		D		R
O					A			L		I		I
L	A	M	B	E	N	T		S	C	O	R	N
			R		G		D		A			G
D	A	M	A	G	E		E	X	C	I	S	E
E			G		R		A		H			
S	M	A	S	H		A	D	R	E	N	A	L
P		D		E			E					A
I		L		S	K	I	N	F	L	I	N	T
S	K	I		S			D		E			H
E		B	U	E	N	O	S	A	I	R	E	S

86

S	A	C	R	I	F	I	C	I	N	G		P
Y			O		I		A		O			I
S	M	O	U	L	D	E	R		N	E	A	R
T			G		G		G		E			A
E	F	F	E	T	E		O	U	T	P	U	T
M		L			T					O		E
	D	A	N	E	S		P	A	D	R	E	
F		I					L			C		G
R	E	L	I	E	F		A	N	C	H	O	R
E			N		L		S		O			E
E	N	I	D		U	L	T	I	M	A	T	E
L			I		F		E		M			C
Y		P	E	R	F	O	R	M	A	N	C	E

87

S	C	A	R	C	E		A	C	A	C	I	A
T				A		H		A				G
U	N	D	E	R	W	E	I	G	H	T		R
R		I		D		L		E		R		E
D	E	S	T	I	N	E	D		W	E	R	E
Y		B		G		N		M		A		D
	R	E	H	A	B		C	A	N	D	Y	
B		L		N		H		G		M		O
U	N	I	T		T	A	X	A	T	I	O	N
R		E		S		V		Z		L		E
I		F	A	T	H	E	R	I	N	L	A	W
E				U		N		N				A
S	A	L	I	N	E		B	E	A	U	T	Y

88

S	C	A	N	T	Y		C	R	A	D	L	E
C		M		E			E		N			A
A	B	O	U	N	D		M		T			S
L		N			E	Y	E	S	I	G	H	T
D	I	G	S		L		N		P		O	
	N		M	A	E	S	T	R	O		M	
A	D	Z	E		T		M		D	I	A	Z
	U		L	E	E	T	I	D	E		G	
	C		L		R		X		S	T	E	M
N	E	G	A	T	I	V	E			W		A
O			R		O		R	A	T	I	O	N
V			A		U			T		C		G
A	B	A	T	E	S		S	E	R	E	N	E

Solutions

Solutions

93

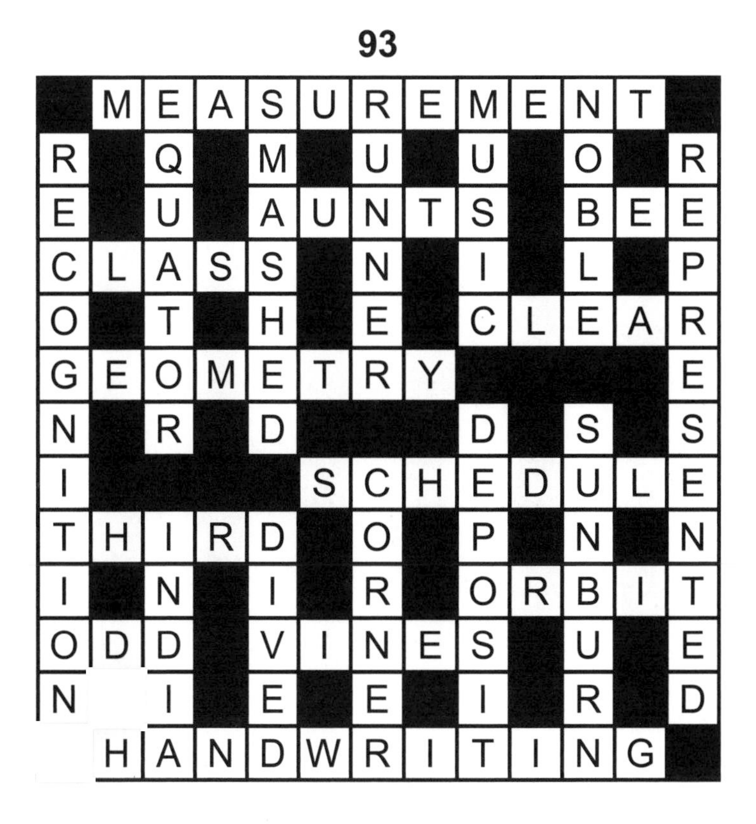

94

B M H CHICKEN
OREGANO E E
D T R R WORSE
YIELD POE N D
O P U DWELL
SURPRISED L E
E E I S
N F SEMANTICS
SHEDS O G N
U D EAU RIDER
OVOID S I E A
U R SYNONYM
SHACKLE G T P

95

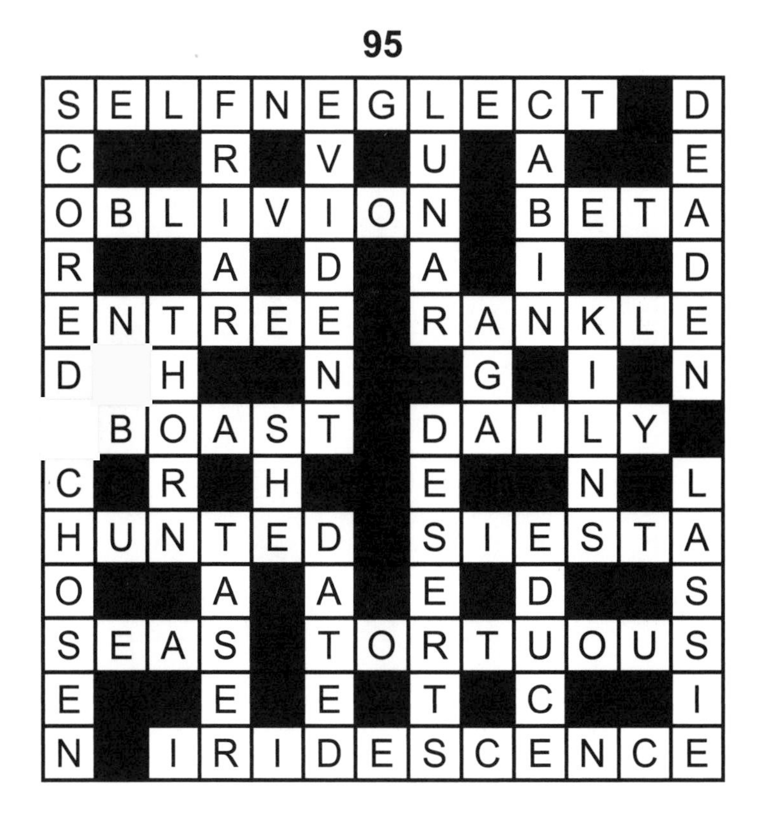

96

Solutions

97

98

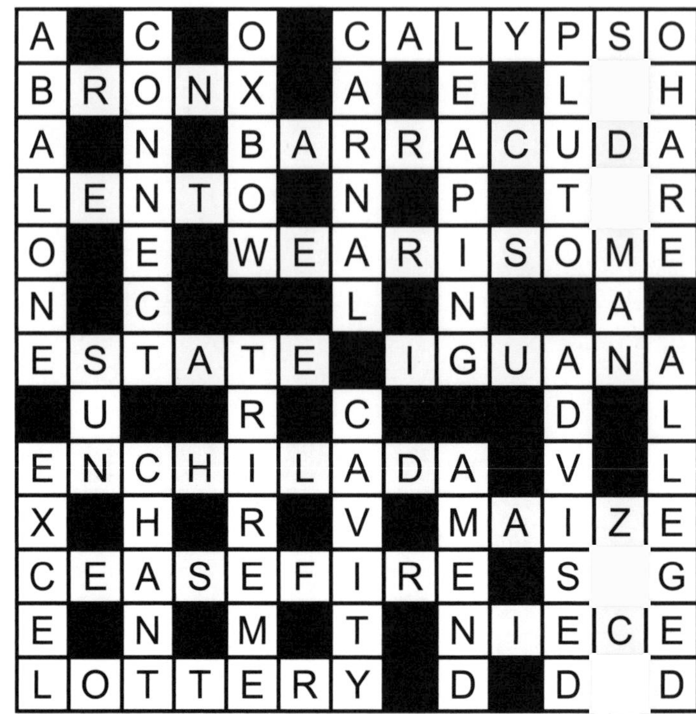

99

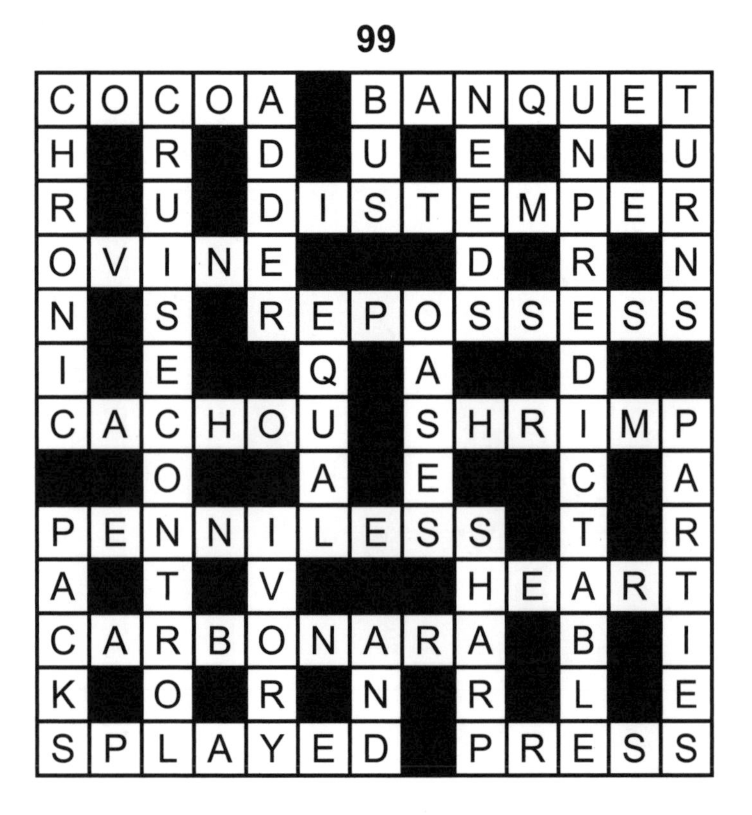

100

Solutions

101

P	A	R	K		B	R	A	C	E	L	E	T
Y		O		E		H		O		A		R
J	O	U	R	N	E	Y		N	E	R	V	E
A		N		C		T		G		G		E
M	U	D	D	Y		H	A	R	N	E	S	S
A				C		M		A		S		
S	U	B	T	L	E		S	T	A	T	U	S
		R		O		A		U				Y
S	T	E	P	P	E	D		L	O	S	E	S
T		A		E		M		A		I		T
A	C	T	E	D		I	N	T	E	N	S	E
M		H		I		R		E		K		M
P	A	S	S	A	G	E	S		A	S	K	S

102

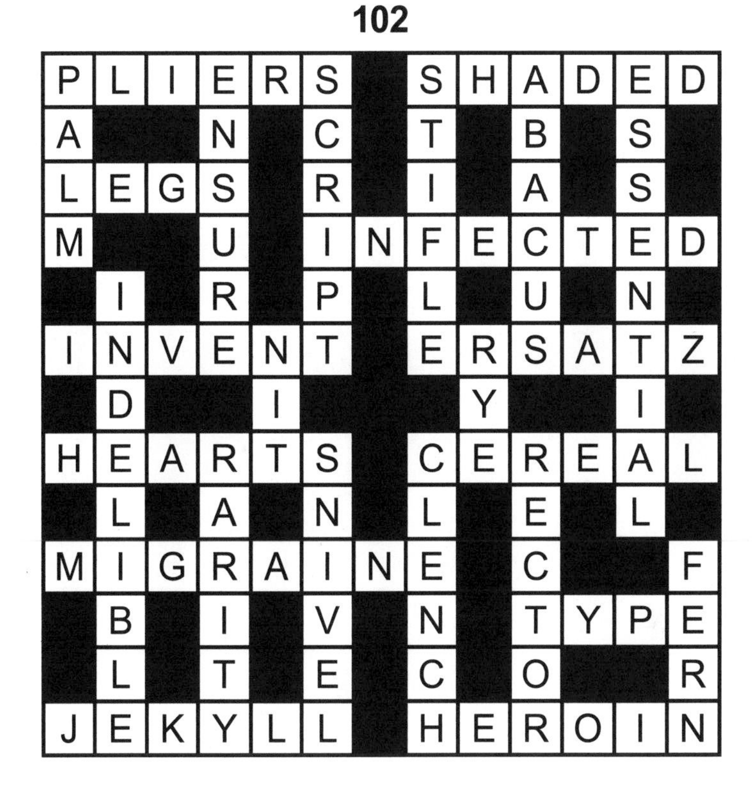

103

P	I	E	S		M	O	C	C	A	S	I	N
O		M		D		H		O		E		O
S	T	A	D	I	U	M		N	I	G	H	T
S		I		S				S		M		E
I	L	L	C	O	N	C	E	I	V	E	D	
B				B		O		D		N		F
L	A	M		E	N	S	U	E		T	E	E
E		I		D		T		R				A
	A	N	T	I	M	A	C	A	S	S	A	R
B		U		E				B		K		L
O	F	T	E	N		V	I	L	L	A	G	E
I		E		C		I		E		T		S
L	A	S	V	E	G	A	S		G	E	M	S

104

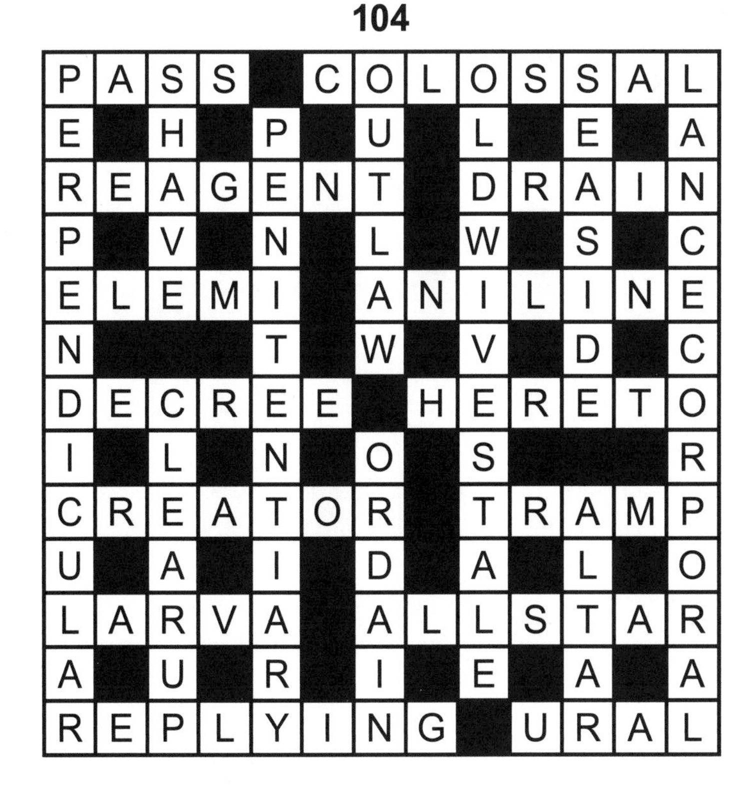

Solutions

105

S	A	C	K	■	A	N	C	H	O	R	E	D
T		H	■	S	■	A	■	E	■	U	■	I
E	L	I	C	I	T	S	■	A	M	B	E	R
N		D	■	M	■	S	■	D	■	B	■	T
C	H	E	A	P	■	E	N	Q	U	I	R	Y
I	■	■	■	L	■	R	■	U	■	S	■	■
L	A	T	H	E	R	■	W	A	S	H	E	S
■	■	H	■	M	■	A	■	R	■	■	■	U
S	H	I	N	I	E	R	■	T	W	A	N	G
O		R	■	N	■	I	■	E	■	F	■	G
N	O	S	E	D	■	S	U	R	M	I	S	E
I		T	■	E	■	E	■	S	■	R	■	S
C	A	S	H	D	E	S	K	■	M	E	A	T

106

T	■	M	■	M	■	P	E	D	I	C	A	B
A	D	I	E	U	■	A	■	I	■	L		E
F	■	N	■	F	O	R	E	S	T	A	L	L
F	L	E	E	T	■	I	■	L	■	R	■	L
E	■	R	■	I	N	S	T	I	G	A	T	E
T	■	A	■	■	■	H	■	K	■	■	O	■
A	S	L	E	E	P	■	T	E	M	P	E	R
■	P	■	■	P	■	T	■	■	■	L	■	E
S	A	C	R	I	F	I	C	E	■	A	■	L
O	■	R	■	S	■	N	■	M	A	N	I	A
C	O	U	R	T	S	H	I	P	■	E	■	T
K	■	M	■	L	■	A	■	T	I	T	L	E
S	U	B	J	E	C	T	■	Y	■	S		D

107

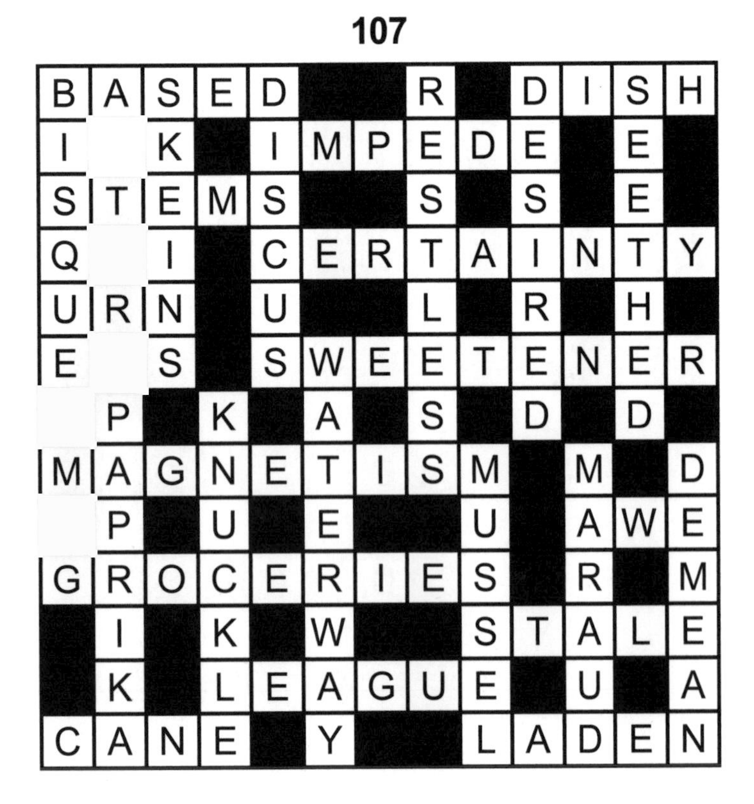

108

Solutions

109

S	O	P	R	A	N	O		B		M		B
E		O		X		W	A	R	F	A	R	E
A	I	R	L	I	N	E		A		K		A
M		T		O		D		V		E		R
E	N	I	G	M	A		C	O	A	R	S	E
N		C			I		U					R
	W	O	B	B	L	E	B	O	A	R	D	
B					E		I			E		R
A	C	C	O	R	D		T	I	S	S	U	E
B		R		O		B		N		T		P
O		E		G		I	T	E	M	I	S	E
O	B	S	C	E	N	E		P		V		N
N		S		R		R	E	T	R	E	A	T

110

111

C	L	A	N	G		K			F		R	
A		L		L		I	D	Y	L	L	I	C
S	T	A	T	U	R	E			E		V	
H		R		T		V	I	N	T	N	E	R
F		M			M		N		C		R	
L	U	S	C	I	O	U	S		H	U	S	H
O			O		U		I		E			I
W	I	N	G		R	E	T	I	R	I	N	G
	C		I		N		U			N		H
F	A	N	T	A	S	Y		D		S		N
	R		A			A	P	O	S	T	L	E
D	U	S	T	B	I	N		V		I		S
	S		E			K		E	L	L	I	S

112

Solutions

113

B	A	N	G	E	D		C		W		S	
	M		U		E	G	O	T	I	S	T	S
D	U	R	E	S	S		G		D		A	
	S		S		C	A	S	S	E	T	T	E
G	E	Y	S	E	R				N		E	
Y					I	N	C	R	E	A	S	E
B			B		B		O		D			T
E	T	H	E	R	E	A	L					A
	O		A				D	I	S	P	E	L
E	M	E	R	I	T	U	S		I		X	
	B		D		H		O	P	T	O	U	T
H	O	T	E	L	I	E	R		A		D	
	Y		D		N		E	E	R	I	E	R

114

S	A	P	I	E	N	T		P		F		B
N		R				H	A	U	L	A	G	E
I	C	E	F	L	O	E		R		C		A
F		P		U		S	O	L	V	E	N	T
F	O	A	M	S		I						L
		R		A	S	S	E	R	T	I	V	E
D		E		K				U		N		S
R	E	D	H	A	N	D	E	D		C		
U						I		D	E	I	G	N
N	E	R	V	O	U	S		E		S		I
K		A		B		U	K	R	A	I	N	E
E	M	P	R	E	S	S				V		C
N		T		Y		E	X	T	R	E	M	E

115

	S	T	E	A	L	S		C	O	Y	P	U
N		R		R		N		H		A		N
E	N	U	N	C	I	A	T	E		R		I
W		E				K		L	E	N	I	N
T	I	R	E	D	N	E	S	S		S		T
E			L			D		E				E
S	T	U	M	P	S		V	A	P	O	U	R
T				A		N			U			E
A		A		C	H	E	S	T	N	U	T	S
M	I	A	M	I		G				B		T
E		R		F	L	A	G	S	T	O	N	E
N		O		I		T		A		A		D
T	O	N	I	C		E	N	T	I	T	Y	

116

Solutions

117

B	E	C	O	M	E		C	A	L	L	U	S
A		H		O		S		M		A		P
T	R	A	I	N	E	E		O		C		O
T		I		T		L	A	N	T	E	R	N
L	U	R	C	H		F		G				G
E		M				I		S	P	A	T	E
		A		E	M	M	E	T		B		
B	O	N	E	S		P				R		D
R				S		O		S	T	A	K	E
E	N	D	L	E	S	S		E		S		C
A		A		N		E	D	I	F	I	C	E
S		R		C		D		N		V		I
T	I	T	L	E	S		B	E	H	E	S	T

118

B	I	D	S		M	I	S	H	M	A	S	H
R			A		O		T		E		U	
I	D	E	N	T	I	T	Y		D	U	C	T
D			J		S		E		I		C	
A	B	R	U	P	T		S	T	A	M	E	N
L			A		E						E	
	C	A	N	O	N		A	C	R	I	D	
	R						D		E			F
T	U	R	N	I	P		J	A	G	G	E	R
	S		O		L		U		U			E
O	A	H	U		U	N	D	U	L	A	T	E
	D		N		M		G		A			Z
F	E	A	S	I	B	L	E		R	U	L	E

119

W	I	L	D	E	Y	E	D		C	U	B	S
I		E		A		N				N		W
C	R	A	P	S		G	E	N	T	I	L	E
K		N		Y		U				T		E
		T		G		L	E	N	I	E	N	T
S	T	O	P	O	F	F		E		D		E
E				I				C				N
L		S		N		H	O	T	R	O	D	S
F	A	T	I	G	U	E		A		C		
L		R				R		R		E		P
E	V	A	S	I	O	N		I	G	L	O	O
S		T				I		N		O		N
S	W	A	N		T	A	P	E	S	T	R	Y

120

Solutions

121

C	A	F	E		O	C	C	U	P	A	N	T
A		R		A		O		N		U		U
S	T	E	A	M	E	R		S	U	G	A	R
H		Y		B		P		U		M		K
C	O	A	T	I		S	E	R	V	E	R	
R				D		E		P		N		C
O	P	E	N	E	D		G	R	A	T	E	R
P		L		X		W		I				E
	S	E	T	T	E	E		S	A	I	L	S
C		C		R		D		I		M		C
L	E	T	G	O		D	E	N	T	A	T	E
E		O		U		E		G		G		N
F	I	R	E	S	I	D	E		M	E	L	T

122

S	E	X	T	E	T		T	R	E	M	O	R
W			R		H		A		W			O
I	N	V	A	D	E		G		E			L
G			V		I	N	S	C	R	I	B	E
	S		E		R			H			U	
S	T	A	L	L	S		S	I	L	E	N	T
	A			I				N			K	
A	P	L	O	M	B		T	A	R	G	E	T
	L			I			I		W		R	
S	E	D	I	T	I	O	N		A			A
O			F		S		S	Y	N	T	A	X
R			F		L		E		D			L
E	N	Z	Y	M	E		L	I	A	B	L	E

123

H	A	L	F	W	I	T		B	L	I	S	S
E		E		O		R		O		N		P
R	E	V	E	R	B	E	R	A	T	E		O
O				T		A				L		O
I	R	I	S	H		T	R	A	D	E	I	N
C		N		L		Y		D		G		
S	H	A	V	E	N		I	M	P	A	L	E
		N		S		I		I		N		S
C	R	I	M	S	O	N		S	I	T	E	S
A		M				S		S				E
R		A	W	E	S	T	R	I	C	K	E	N
D		T		E		E		O		E		C
S	T	E	A	L		P	E	N	A	N	C	E

124

B	L	A	N	C	H	E		A	Z	T	E	C
E		W		A		U		L		A		R
C	O	N	T	R	A	C	T	I	O	N		U
O				T		L				G		S
M	A	C	A	W		I	N	S	P	E	C	T
E		O		H		D		T		R		
S	O	N	N	E	T		B	A	S	I	N	S
		S		E		P		G		N		A
S	E	T	T	L	E	R		E	V	E	N	T
M		R				O		D				I
E		A	C	C	O	M	M	O	D	A	T	E
L		I		U		P		O		C		T
T	U	N	E	R		T	E	R	S	E	L	Y

Solutions

125

B	R	A	N	D	I	S	H		S	P	I	N
U		I		I		K				Y		E
T	E	R	R	A	P	I	N			R		T
T		T		D		T	O	R	M	E	N	T
O	P	I	N	E			T					L
N		G		M	E	G	A	C	Y	C	L	E
		H			U		R			H		
A	T	T	O	R	N	E	Y	S		L		F
E					U			C	H	O	R	E
R	E	S	P	E	C	T		R		R		W
A		I			H	O	M	I	C	I	D	E
T		G				M		B		N		S
E	C	H	O		R	E	V	E	R	E	N	T

126

M	I	G	H	T	Y		D	A	R	N	E	D
O				H		R		G				E
D	E	T	E	R	I	O	R	A	T	E		N
I		R		O		B		R		X		I
F	R	A	C	T	I	O	N		S	T	Y	E
Y		N		T		T		G		R		R
	P	S	A	L	M		P	A	G	E	R	
D		C		E		C		N		M		A
I	D	E	S		S	H	A	G	G	I	E	R
N		N		U		E		R		S		G
N		D	I	F	F	E	R	E	N	T	L	Y
E				O		K		N				L
R	A	D	I	S	H		D	E	C	I	D	E

127

S	H	E	L	T	E	R		S	W	A	T	H
T		M		U		E		W			R	
U	P	P	E	R		S	W	A	G	M	A	N
F		E		B		I		M			M	
F	A	R	M	I	N	G		P	O	P	P	Y
E		O		N		N					L	
D	A	R	K	E	N		C	A	N	C	E	R
	C					I		V		O		E
D	E	I	S	M		T	R	E	B	L	E	D
	T			I		A		N		L		T
C	O	L	O	N	E	L		G	H	A	N	A
	N			U		I		E		G		P
B	E	A	T	S		C	O	R	T	E	G	E

128

M	O	B	I	L	E		M		A		P	
I		L			M	O	O	N	B	E	A	M
S		A			B		T		E		T	
S	U	B	D	U	E		T	E	L	L	E	R
E			I		R		O				R	
S	T	A	V	E		B	E	T	T	I	N	G
	A		O		B		S		I		A	
S	T	A	T	I	O	N		H	E	L	L	O
	T				U		V		R			P
R	E	T	A	I	N		I	N	S	E	C	T
	R		V		C		N			X		I
D	E	L	I	V	E	R	Y			A		C
	D		D		R		L	I	T	M	U	S

Solutions

129

130

131

132

Solutions

133

B	U	S	S	T	O	P		B	R	A	S	S
A		U		I		E			A			N
L	I	P		G	U	E	R	R	I	L	L	A
L		R		H		K			M			K
A	V	E	R	T			L		E	P	E	E
S		M		S	A	L	O	O	N			
T	H	E	M		C		S		T	O	M	B
			O	T	I	O	S	E		U		E
R	A	I	N		D			G	O	T	A	T
E			I			B		G		L		W
M	O	N	T	B	L	A	N	C		I	C	E
I			O			K		U		V		E
T	A	R	R	Y		U	M	P	T	E	E	N

134

P	O	S	S	I	B	I	L	I	T	I	E	S
I			A		L		A			N		E
S	A	C	S		U		S	T	R	I	F	E
T			S	O	N	G	S			T		M
O	K	A	Y		T		O	B	L	I	G	E
N		L					E			A		D
	N	A	T	A	L		S	I	X	T	Y	
G		B		E						E		D
A	D	A	G	E	S		M		T	S	A	R
E		S			S	C	A	L	Y			Y
L	I	T	T	L	E		N		P	A	I	R
I		E			N		G		E			O
C	O	R	R	E	S	P	O	N	D	E	N	T

135

F	R	A	N	C		S	M	I	T	T	E	N
A		L		A		H			O		A	
L		M		L		E		B	E	I	G	E
S	H	O	U	L	D	E	R		C		L	
E		N		I		T		J	A	D	E	D
H	E	D	O	N	I	S	M		P			I
O		S		G				S		C		M
O			D		V	E	N	E	R	A	T	E
D	R	U	I	D		C		Y		N		N
	E		V		C	L	E	M	A	T	I	S
O	T	H	E	R		A		O		O		I
	R		R			I		U		N		O
C	O	R	S	A	I	R		R	E	S	I	N

136

W	H	O	O	P		S	E	R	R	I	E	D
A		D		A	S	P		O		R		O
S	P	I	E	L		A		A	B	O	U	T
H		U		E		C		C		N		S
A		M	O	T	H	E	R	H	O	O	D	
B				T		S				R		D
L	Y	C	H	E	E		W	H	E	E	Z	E
E		L				S		I				S
	M	A	L	E	F	A	C	T	O	R		E
B		V		R		X		L		E		R
O	U	I	J	A		O		I	N	E	R	T
Y		E		S		N	H	S		V		E
S	U	R	G	E	R	Y		T	R	E	A	D

Solutions

137

H	O	N	E	S	T		A		A		C	
Y		U			A	L	L	C	L	E	A	R
P	U	M	P		C		L		M		N	
N		B	A	S	K	E	T		S	A	N	D
O			T		Y		O				O	
S	L	E	E	K		E	L	E	G	A	N	T
I			N		T		D		R			E
S	H	U	T	O	U	T		P	A	I	N	S
	O				M		F		V			T
T	O	S	S		B	O	R	D	E	R		A
	R		H		L		Y		L	A	S	T
M	A	G	I	C	E	Y	E			N		O
	Y		P		R		R	O	S	T	E	R

138

U	P	S	E	T		T	O	U	R	I	S	T
N		E		U		R			I		T	
D		S		R		A		S	C	R	E	W
R	E	S	T	R	A	I	N		H		A	
E		I		E		N		C	L	U	M	P
S	H	O	R	T	E	S	T		Y			R
S		N		S				C		T		E
E			O		S	P	L	A	S	H	E	S
D	A	I	R	Y		O		P		E		I
	P		I		M	U	T	T	E	R	E	D
B	A	D	G	E		R		U		E		E
	R		I			E		R		B		N
S	T	U	N	N	E	D		E	G	Y	P	T

139

M	A	S	C	A	R	A		O	M	I	T	S
E		U		L		N			A			E
R	I	P		I	N	T	E	G	R	A	T	E
M		P		G		E			Q			D
A	D	O	R	N			C		U	G	L	Y
I		S		S	T	R	O	K	E			
D	E	E	P		I		S		E	D	D	Y
			R	E	L	A	Y	S		I		A
V	I	S	A		T			L	E	P	E	R
I			T			B		E		L		D
S	C	A	T	T	E	R	E	D		O	V	A
O			L			A		G		M		G
R	O	D	E	O		G	R	E	N	A	D	E

140

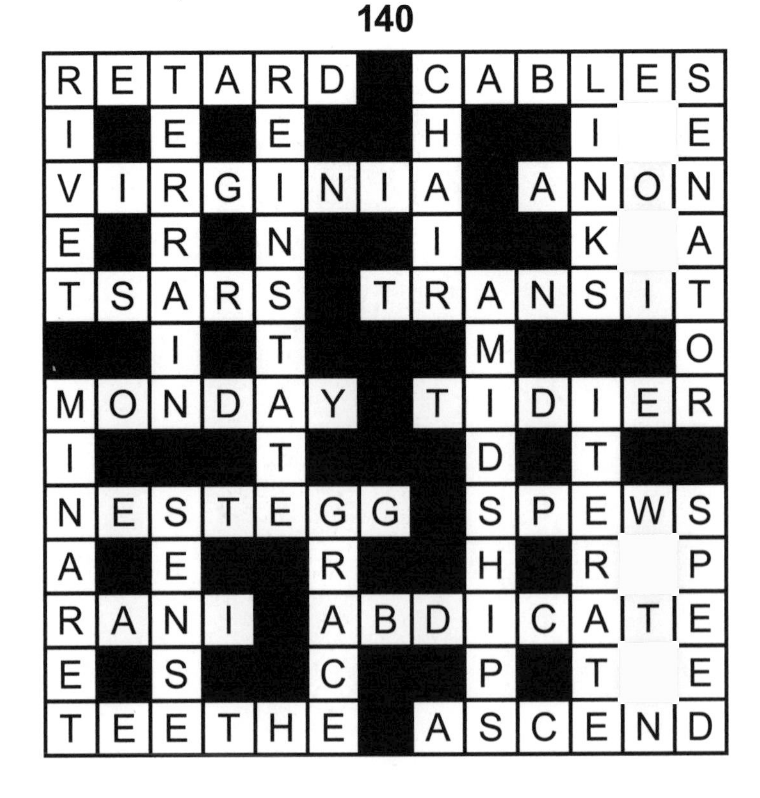

R	E	T	A	R	D		C	A	B	L	E	S
I		E		E			H			I		E
V	I	R	G	I	N	I	A		A	N	O	N
E		R		N			I			K		A
T	S	A	R	S		T	R	A	N	S	I	T
		I		T				M				O
M	O	N	D	A	Y		T	I	D	I	E	R
I				T				D		T		
N	E	S	T	E	G	G		S	P	E	W	S
A		E			R			H		R		P
R	A	N	I		A	B	D	I	C	A	T	E
E		S			C			P		T		E
T	E	E	T	H	E		A	S	C	E	N	D

Solutions

141

R	E	S	I	L	I	E	N	T	■	S	E	E
U		U	■	U	■	■	■	R	■	K	■	A
S	O	L	E	M	N	■	B	O	R	I	N	G
K		T	■	B	■	P	■	L	■	M	■	L
	U	R	S	A	■	E	C	L	I	P	S	E
A	■	Y	■	G	■	R	■	■	■	Y	■	E
L	■	■	C	O	N	F	U	S	E	■	■	Y
L	■	H	■	■	■	O	■	U	■	S	■	E
T	R	A	I	L	E	R	■	R	A	I	D	■
H		M	■	A	■	M	■	V	■	F	■	R
E	X	P	I	R	E	■	B	I	S	T	R	O
R		E	■	C	■	■	■	V	■	E	■	O
E	A	R	■	H	O	T	H	E	A	D	E	D

142

C	A	S	T	L	E	■	B	■	C	■	■	C
■	R	■	■	I	■	B	A	L	E	F	U	L
C	O	N	V	E	Y	■	I	■	N	■	■	O
■	S	■	■	G	■	G	L	O	T	T	I	S
T	E	A	S	E	L	■	■	■	U	■	■	E
R	■	■	P	■	A	N	G	E	R	■	■	N
A	N	N	A	■	I	■	R	■	I	D	L	E
N	■	■	C	O	R	G	I	■	O	■	■	S
S	■	■	E	■	■	■	M	A	N	T	I	S
P	A	S	S	I	N	G	■	G	■	■	D	■
O	■	■	H	■	E	■	C	A	M	P	E	R
S	H	R	I	V	E	L	■	T	■	■	A	■
E	■	■	P	■	D	■	G	E	N	T	L	Y

143

144

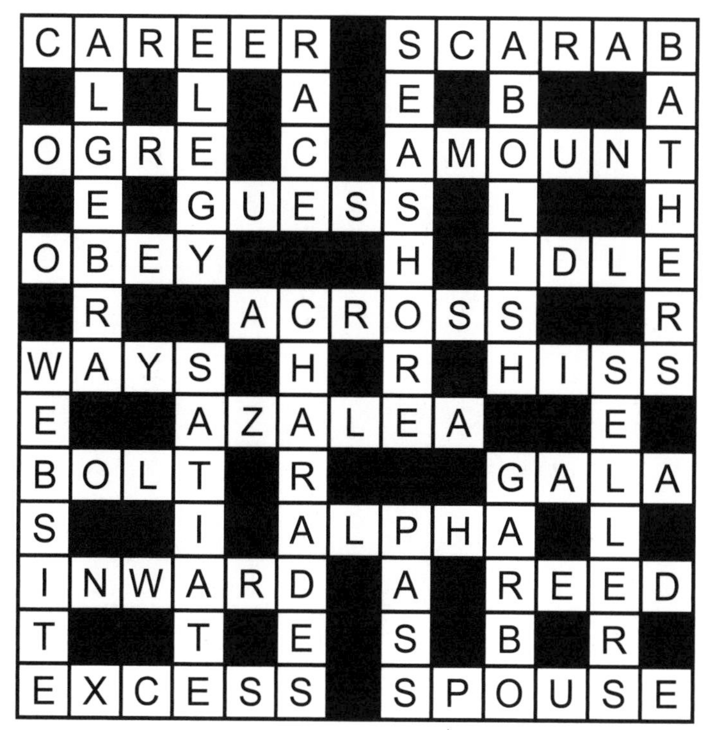

Solutions

145

B		S	■	P	■	U	N	C	R	O	S	S
O	V	E	R	R	U	N	■	■	■	N	■	U
S		A	■	E	■	L	■	S	O	L	E	S
S	T	A	I	D	■	E	M	U	■	I	■	P
■	■	I	■	E	■	S	■	B	I	N	G	E
W	O	R	M	C	A	S	T	S	■	E	■	N
O	■	■	■	E	■	■	■	T	■	■	■	S
N	■	R	■	S	U	B	M	A	R	I	N	E
D	E	E	D	S	■	U	■	N	■	T	■	■
R		T	■	O	W	N	■	T	I	A	R	A
O	S	I	E	R	■	Y	■	I	■	L	■	C
U		N	■	■	■	I	M	A	G	I	N	E
S	H	A	K	E	U	P	■	L	■	C	■	R

146

A	B	U	S	E	R	■	C	A	C	T	U	S
F	■	■	■	N	■	U	■	G	■	■	■	A
R	E	P	E	T	I	T	I	O	U	S	■	C
A	■	R	■	R	■	T	■	G	■	T	■	H
I	S	O	L	A	T	E	D	■	U	R	G	E
D	■	B	■	N	■	R	■	P	■	E		T
■	T	O	R	C	H	■	B	A	N	N	S	
W	■	S	■	E	■	R	■	S	■	U		N
A	R	C	H	■	G	E	M	S	T	O	N	E
R	■	I	■	T	■	T	■	P	■	U		E
S	■	S	T	A	R	C	R	O	S	S	E	D
A	■	■	■	P	■	H	■	R	■	■	■	L
W	E	A	V	E	R	■	A	T	H	O	M	E

147

R	E	B	U	I	L	D	■	J	■	B	U	S
	D	■	■	L	■	A	R	O	S	E	■	E
S	I	M	I	L	A	R	■	E	■	C	■	X
	T	■	■	F	■	K	■	Y	E	A	S	T
M	I	S	T	A	K	E	N	■	■	U	■	A
	O	■	■	T	■	N	■	M	■	S	■	N
S	N	I	P	E	R	■	L	A	T	E	S	T
A	■	N	■	D	■	J	■	T	■	■	H	■
T	■	N	■	■	D	E	C	E	A	S	E	D
S	A	I	N	T	■	S	■	R	■	■	A	■
U	■	N	■	E	■	T	H	I	R	S	T	Y
M	■	G	R	A	Z	E	■	A	■	■	H	■
A	S	S	■	T	■	R	E	L	A	X	E	D

148

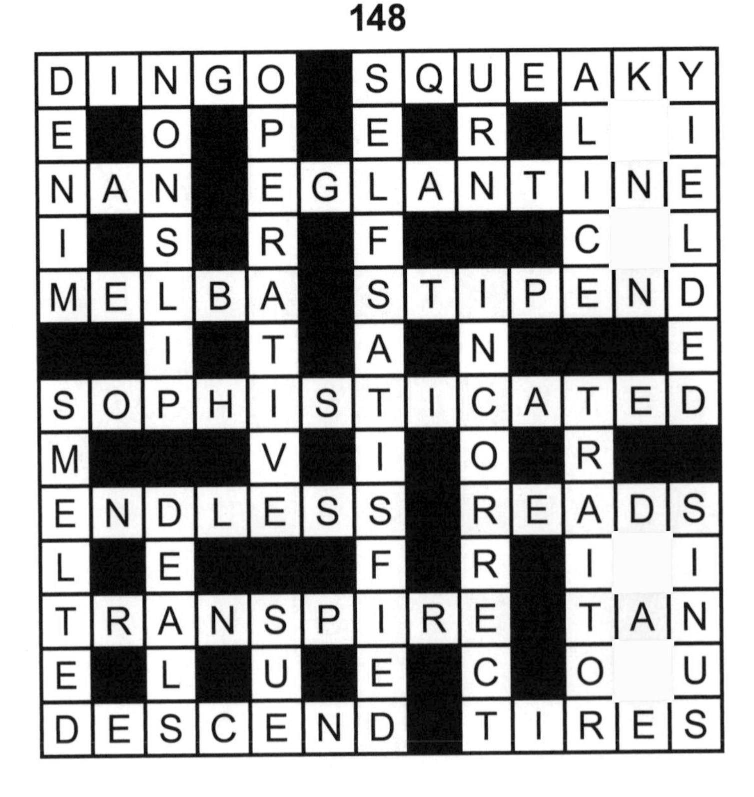

D	I	N	G	O	■	S	Q	U	E	A	K	Y
E	■	O	■	P	■	E	■	R	■	L		I
N	A	N	■	E	G	L	A	N	T	I	N	E
I	■	S	■	R	■	F	■	■	■	C		L
M	E	L	B	A	■	S	T	I	P	E	N	D
■	■	I	■	T	■	A	■	N	■	■	■	E
S	O	P	H	I	S	T	I	C	A	T	E	D
M	■	■	■	V	■	I	■	O	■	R	■	■
E	N	D	L	E	S	S	■	R	E	A	D	S
L	■	E	■	■	■	F	■	R	■	I		I
T	R	A	N	S	P	I	R	E	■	T	A	N
E	■	L	■	U	■	E	■	C	■	O		U
D	E	S	C	E	N	D	■	T	I	R	E	S

Solutions

149

C	H	A	N	G	E		D		T		U	
L		J			S	U	R	R	O	U	N	D
E	X	A	M		T		Y		S		F	
M		R	A	C	E	M	E		S	E	A	R
A			T		R		Y				I	
T	A	R	R	Y		B	E	R	S	E	R	K
I			O		D	U	D		K			I
S	C	E	N	T	E	D		M	A	S	O	N
	O				A		E		T			D
I	R	I	S		D	I	A	D	E	M		N
	N		H		E		V		R	A	G	E
D	E	F	I	A	N	C	E			R		S
	R		N		D		S	I	N	E	W	S

150

151

S	H	E	A	R	S		H		A		C	
U		V			C	H	A	T	R	O	O	M
P		E			R		N		I		H	
P	U	R	S	U	E		D	R	A	W	E	R
L			T		W		L				R	
E	S	S	A	Y		S	E	E	S	R	E	D
	E		R		M		R		T		N	
B	A	T	T	L	E	S		P	A	N	T	S
	W				E		L		I			I
L	A	M	E	N	T		I	N	N	I	N	G
	T		S		I		V			N		N
R	E	S	P	O	N	S	E			C		E
	R		Y		G		S	U	N	H	A	T

152

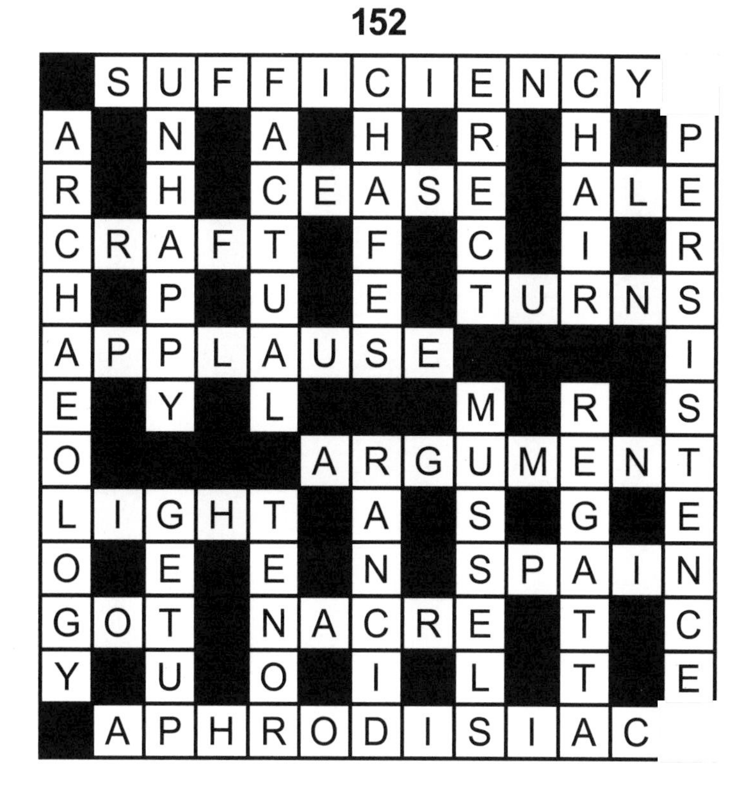

Solutions

153

154

W	Y	S	I	W	Y	G		B		L		B
A		P		I		A	V	O	C	A	D	O
F	R	I	E	N	D	S		A		R		N
F		N		C		P		S		G		N
L	A	D	I	E	S		S	T	O	O	G	E
E		L			U		A					T
	T	E	R	R	E	S	T	R	I	A	L	
B					D		I			S		B
A	C	C	U	S	E		N	A	U	S	E	A
C		E		A		O		I		U		D
K		D		L		D	I	S	H	R	A	G
E	X	A	L	T	E	D		L		E		E
R		R		Y		S	L	E	N	D	E	R

155

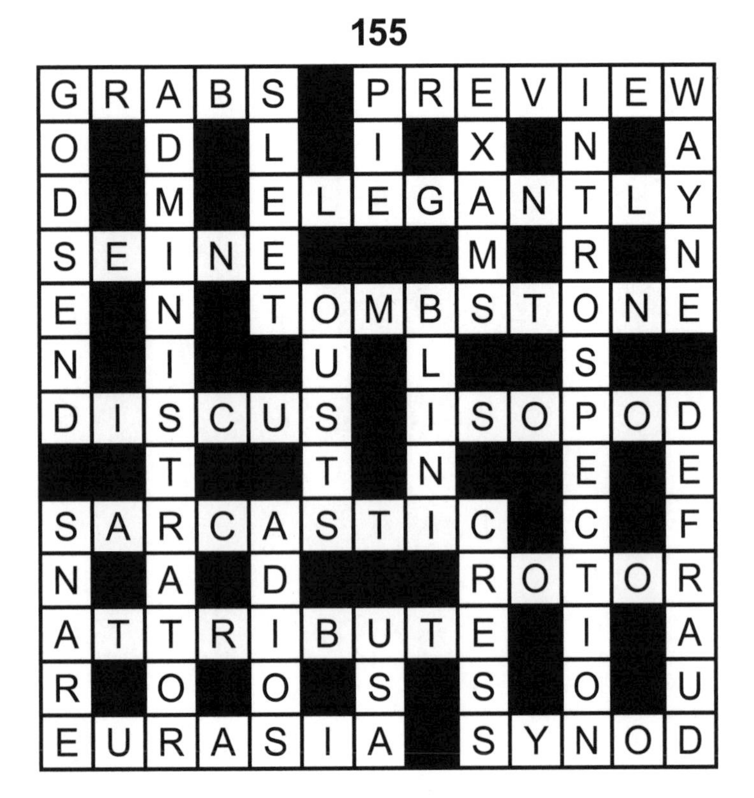

156

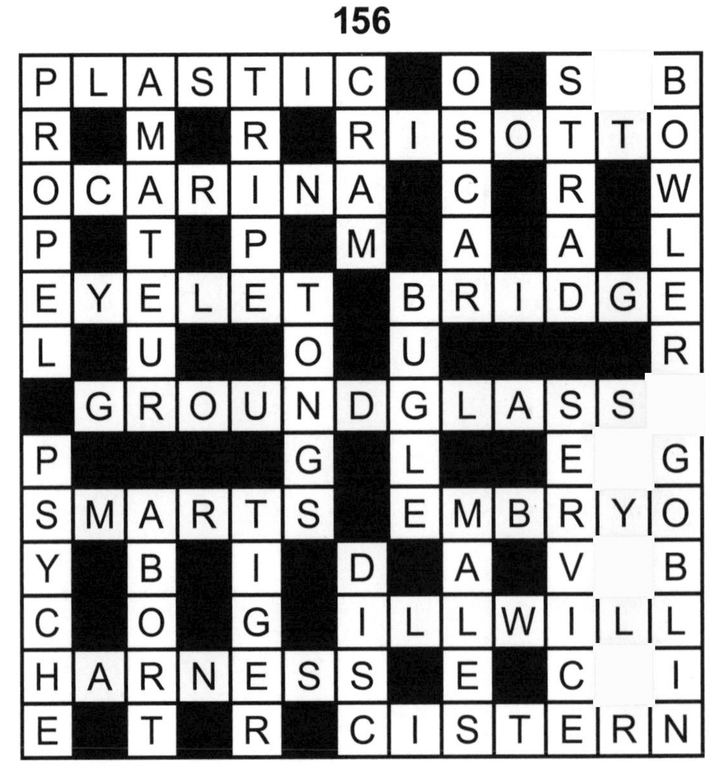

Solutions

157

	A	D	D	L	E	D		S	H	A	R	P
C		I		O		A		U		M		R
R	O	A	D	W	O	R	K	S		I		E
O		N				T		T	A	S	K	S
S	O	A	P	O	P	E	R	A		S		S
S			I			D		I				R
C	O	N	G	E	R		S	N	O	O	Z	E
O				Q		E			P			L
U		M		U	N	D	E	R	T	A	K	E
N	A	I	R	A		I				L		A
T		N		L	I	T	I	G	I	O	U	S
R		I		L		E		U		N		E
Y	U	M	M	Y		D	I	T	H	E	R	

158

M	E	T	R	O	N	O	M	E		S	E	E
A		E		V				L		T		V
D	A	N	C	E	R		P	A	R	A	D	E
E		N		R		G		T		V		R
	P	I	E	D		S	C	E	N	E	R	Y
C		S		U		T				S		O
R			D	E	T	R	A	C	T			N
O		J				I		O		L		E
S	T	E	P	S	O	N		N	E	A	P	
S		W		C		G		F		R		S
I	C	E	C	A	P		D	E	R	I	D	E
N		L		L				S		A		N
G	A	S		P	R	E	S	S	S	T	U	D

159

C	A	M	E		P	A	N	P	I	P	E	S
U		A		S		X		O		U		M
C	O	R	N	I	C	E		L	I	N	G	O
U		K		G				E		G		G
M	I	S	I	N	T	E	R	P	R	E	T	
B				I		Y		O		N		I
E	V	A		F	E	R	N	S		T	O	N
R		M		I		I		I				F
	U	N	A	C	C	E	P	T	A	B	L	E
M		E		A				I		U		R
A	R	S	O	N		G	N	O	C	C	H	I
S		I		C		A		N		K		O
S	C	A	V	E	N	G	E		T	S	A	R

160

Solutions

161

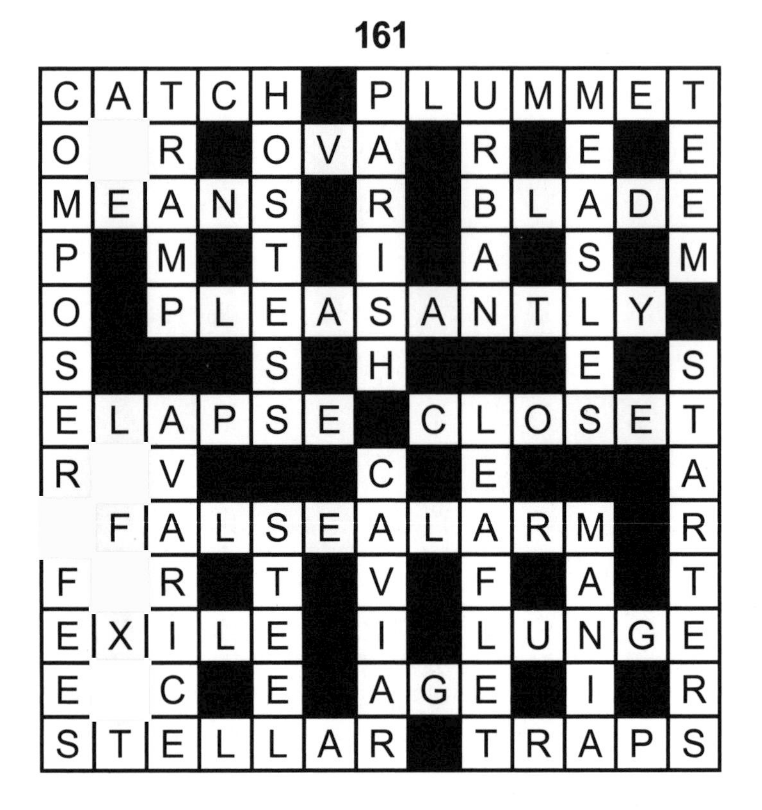

162

163

164

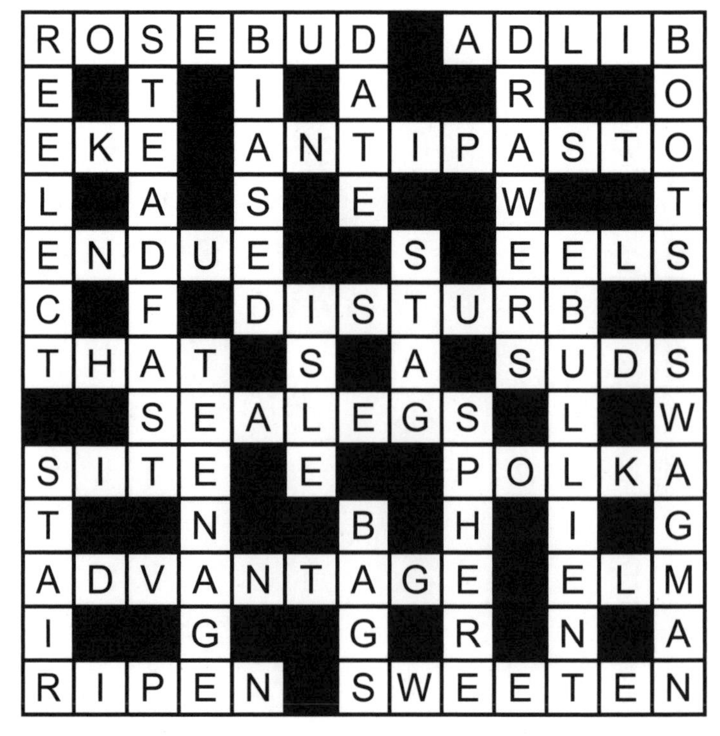

Solutions

165

S	H	R	I	M	P		A		P		M	
H		A			U	P	S	T	R	E	A	M
A	S	P			R		H		I		N	
D		T	H	R	E	A	T		S	L	A	P
E		O			E		R		T		G	
S	C	R	E	E		C	A	B	I	N	E	T
			Y		S		Y		N			
C	O	V	E	R	E	D		H	E	R	B	S
	R		L		T		B			E		Y
H	I	F	I		S	I	E	N	N	A		N
	G		N		A		V			L	I	T
F	I	R	E	S	I	D	E			T		A
	N		R		L		L	A	R	Y	N	X

166

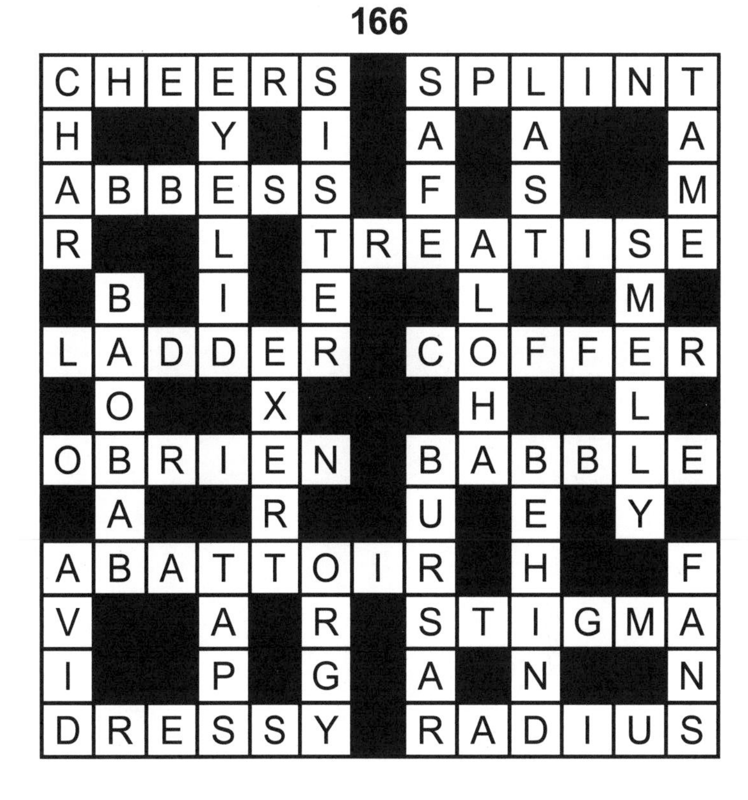

167

C	A	N	C	E	R		S	I	C	K	L	E
	B		O		O		T		O		E	
P	O	N	Y		C	A	R	O	U	S	E	L
	M		N		K		E		N			
B	I	D	E	T		B	A	P	T	I	S	M
	N		S		F		M				U	
N	A	U	S	E	A		E	N	S	U	R	E
	T				T		R		H		R	
B	E	E	S	W	A	X		B	A	C	O	N
			L		L		D		T		G	
F	E	M	I	N	I	N	E		T	R	A	Y
	O		D		S		F		E		T	
I	N	V	E	S	T		T	U	R	N	E	R

168

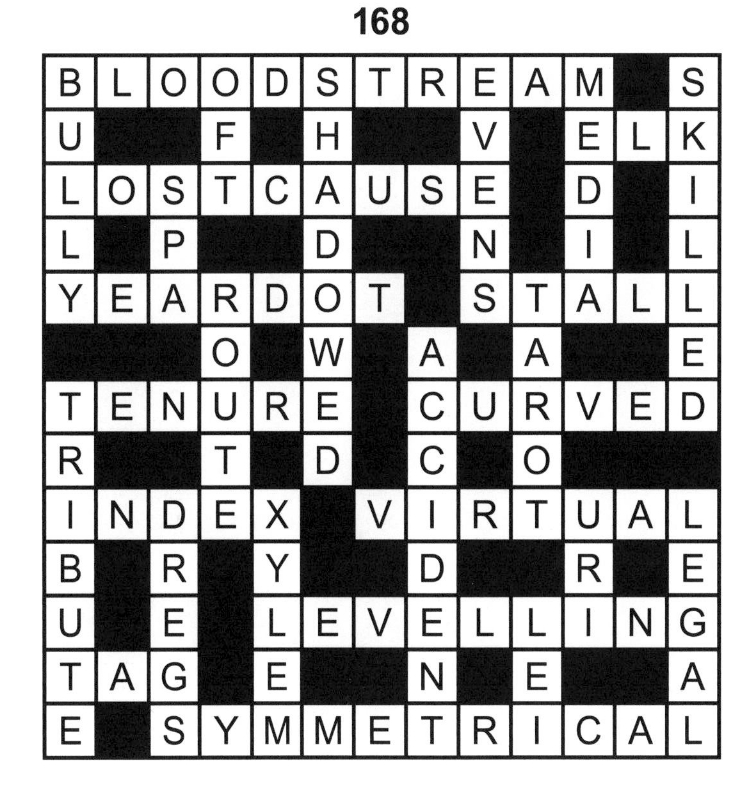

Solutions

169

170

171

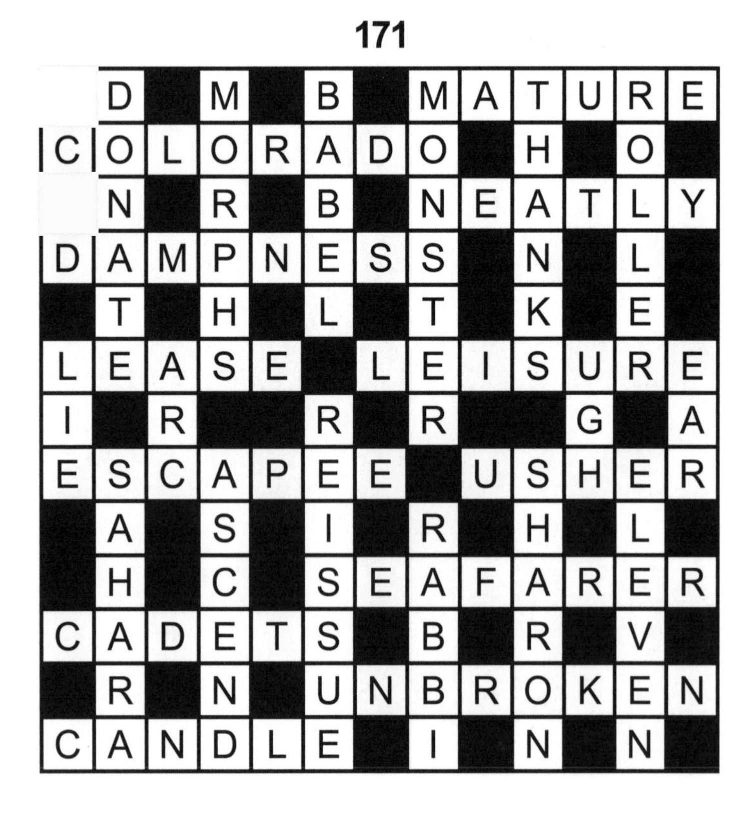

172

Solutions

173

C	O	C	K		T	E	A	B	R	E	A	K
O		H		D		N		U		M		I
S	E	A	B	I	R	D		S	H	E	E	N
M		O		V				I		R		G
E	A	S	T	E	R	S	U	N	D	A	Y	
T				R		A		E		L		K
I	L	L		S	A	L	E	S		D	O	E
C		E		I		S		S				R
	S	A	N	F	R	A	N	C	I	S	C	O
C		N		Y				A		L		S
A	L	I	B	I		C	A	R	N	A	G	E
K		N		N		A		D		T		N
E	N	G	A	G	I	N	G		W	E	R	E

174

L	O	A	T	H	E		P	L	A	S	M	A
I		C		Y			E			T		S
M	E	T	A	P	H	O	R		M	E	N	U
I		R		O		R	I	P		P		N
T	R	E	A	T		B	L	E	S	S	E	D
		S		H				J				E
S	Y	S	T	E	M		C	O	O	L	E	R
L				S				R		E		
I	N	S	P	I	R	E		A	G	O	R	A
P		O		S	O	L		T		N		T
P	A	N	S		O	F	F	I	C	I	A	L
E		I			M			V		N		A
R	E	C	U	R	S		D	E	T	E	R	S

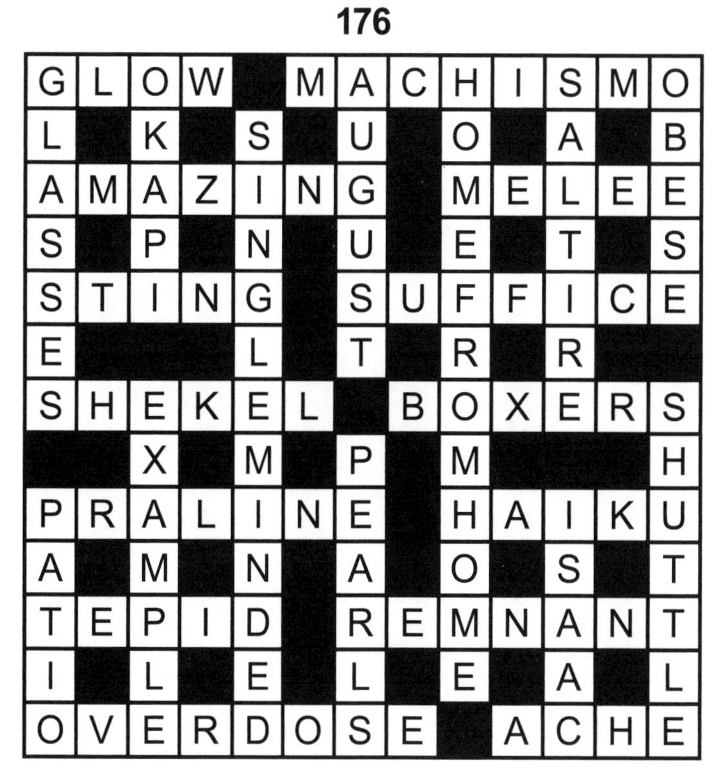

Solutions

177

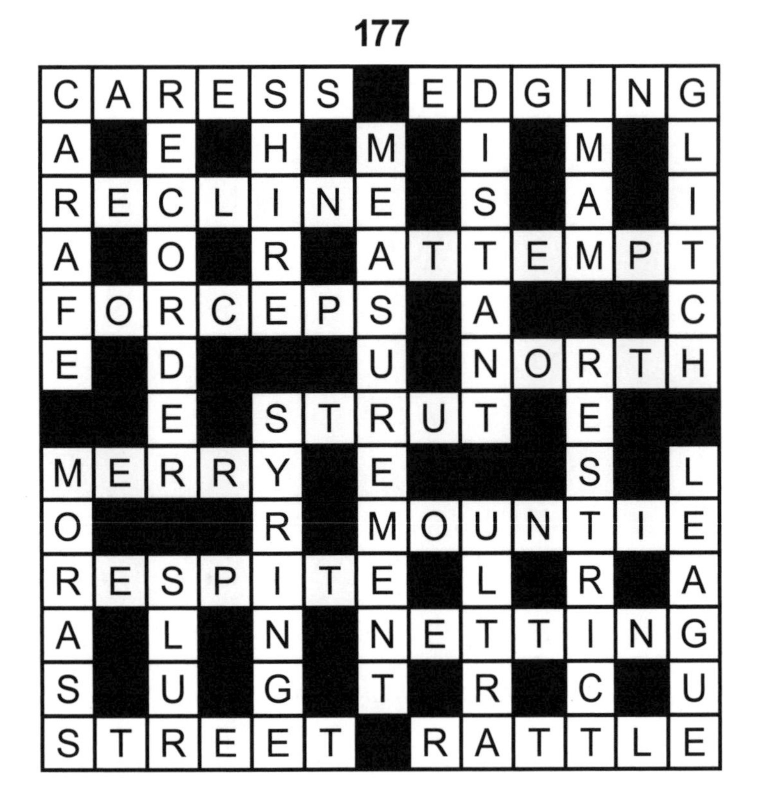

178

MADEIRACAKE A
E X E Y Y M
ELLIPSIS LAMA
K S T T I Z
EARTHY SLEEVE
R O L V D
BADGE DECAY
A M U N O
MOSAIC CURSED
E G A H E I
NOVA SCENARIO
D T T S C U
S NECESSITOUS

179

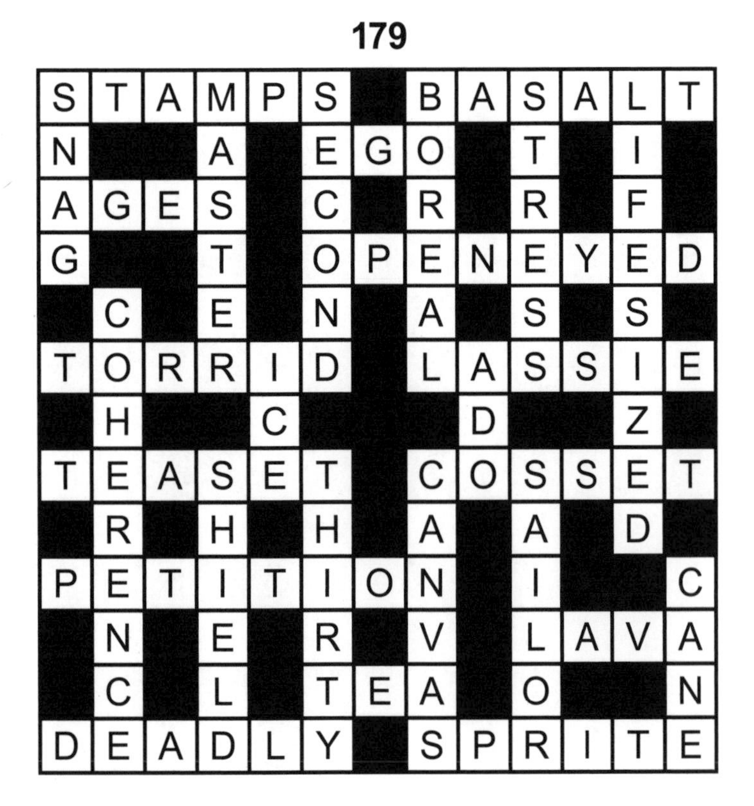

180

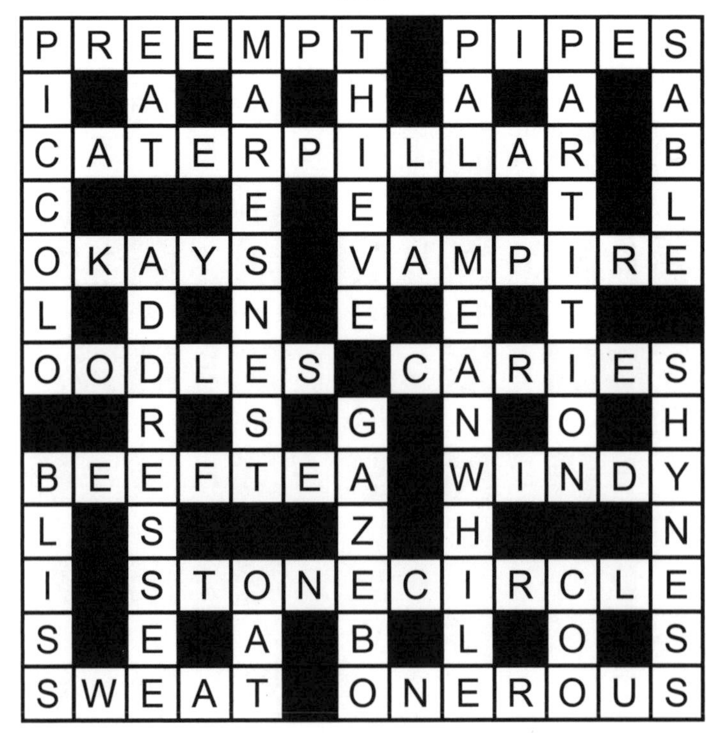

Solutions

181

C	A	R	E	E	N		S	H	R	E	W	D
U		O		V			A		E			E
B	O	W	S	E	R		N		H			N
I		E			E	A	S	T	E	R	L	Y
T	A	R	T		D		A		A		U	
	S		S	C	H	O	L	A	R		S	
B	Y	T	E		E		V		S	C	A	M
	L		T	E	R	R	A	C	E		K	
	U		S		R		D		S	C	A	B
I	M	P	E	T	I	G	O			O		O
B			F		N		R	E	P	A	I	R
I			L		G			R		S		E
S	A	T	Y	R	S		H	A	L	T	E	D

182

G	U	S	T	O		S	P	A	R	I	N	G
A		T		B	A	T		S		L		O
T	U	R	F	S		A		I	N	L	A	W
E		I		C		M		D		I		N
P		P	R	E	F	E	R	E	N	C	E	
O				N		N				I		N
S	U	C	K	E	D		S	C	Y	T	H	E
T		A				T		H				B
	I	N	C	A	P	A	C	I	T	Y		R
B		T		I		R		C		U		A
I	M	A	G	O		T		K	I	C	K	S
D		T		L		A	W	E		C		K
S	E	A	L	I	O	N		N	Y	A	L	A

183

M	A	N	I	C		B			P			B
I		E		L		A	V	E	R	A	G	E
L	E	U		O		S			O			R
L		R		S	P	E	E	D	B	O	A	T
I	N	A	N	E			L		L			H
N		L		D	E	L	I	V	E	R	Y	
G			D		V		T		M			B
	P	R	E	M	I	S	E	S		P		U
B			V		C			A	M	O	U	R
A	D	D	I	C	T	I	O	N		R		D
R			L			C		D		O	W	E
B	U	R	R	I	T	O		A		U		N
S			Y			N		L	I	S	T	S

184

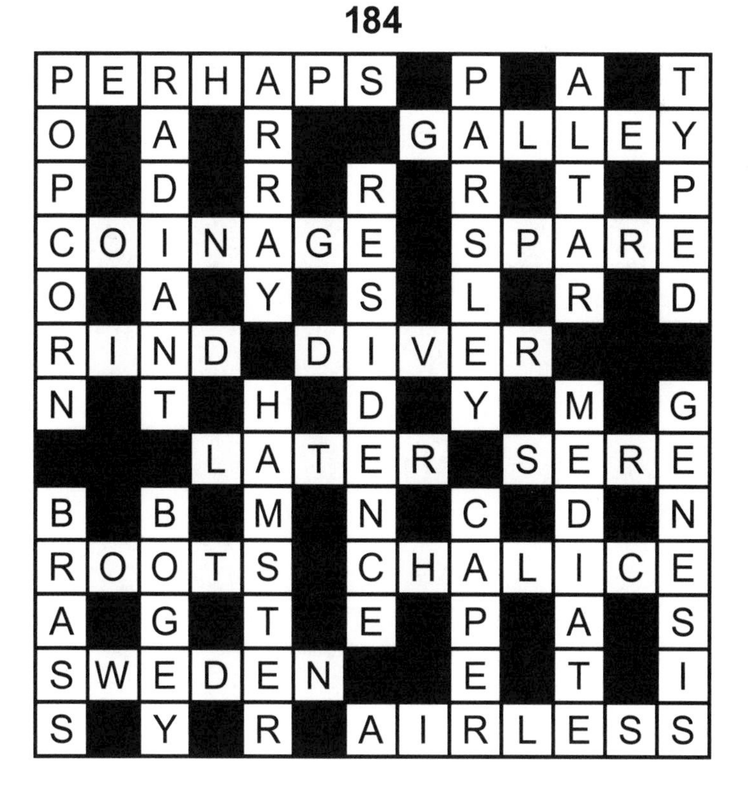

Solutions

185

S	O	B	E	R			F		S	A	S	H
E		A		U	N	D	O	N	E		A	
C	U	R	E	S			R		A		L	
T		B		S	A	T	E	L	L	I	T	E
O	R	E		I			W		A		I	
R		R		A	T	T	A	I	N	D	E	R
	K		T		E		R		T		R	
D	E	T	E	R	R	E	N	T		A		S
	Y		A		M			I		R	O	T
W	H	I	R	L	I	G	I	G		R		A
	O		G		N			H	O	I	S	T
	L		A	R	A	R	A	T		V		U
D	E	N	S		L			S	W	E	D	E

186

187

S	A	C	K		N	E	C	R	O	S	I	S
Y		A		F		G		I		P		L
C	A	R	R	I	E	R		O	M	E	G	A
A		D		R		E		D		C		T
M	O	S	E	S		S	N	E	A	K	Y	
O				T		S		J		L		C
R	E	C	O	R	D		C	A	M	E	R	A
E		U		E		C		N				L
	P	R	E	F	E	R		E	X	T	R	A
S		I		U		U		I		H		M
P	R	O	P	S		M	A	R	T	I	N	I
A		U		A		B		O		N		N
R	E	S	T	L	E	S	S		A	G	U	E

188

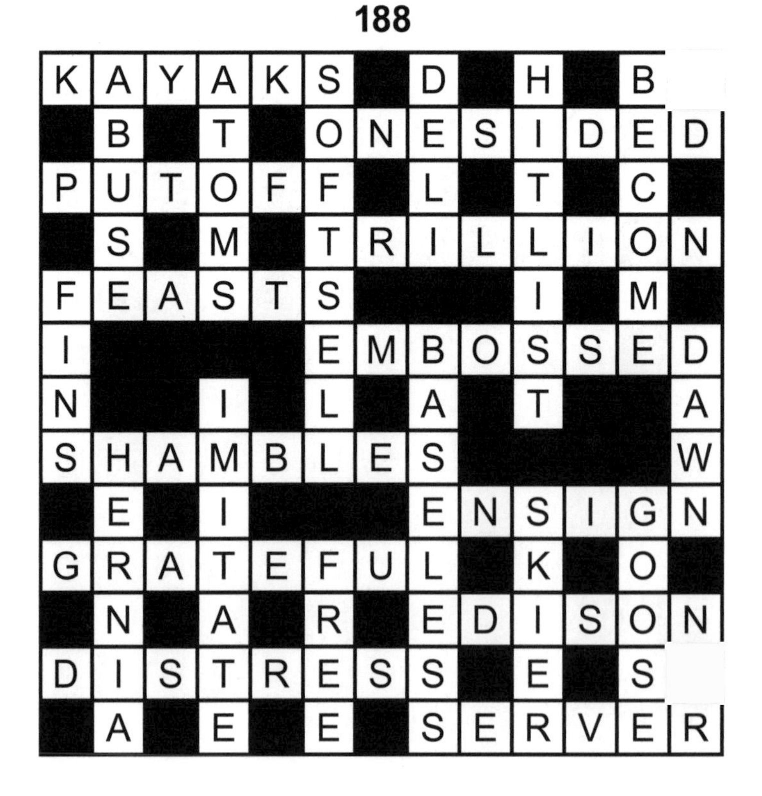

Solutions

189

E	X	C	E	E	D	E	D	■	C	■	H	■
L	■	A	■	■	I	■	R	E	A	S	O	N
O	U	T	S	E	T	■	U	■	N	■	M	■
P	■	■	P	■	C	A	N	I	S	T	E	R
E	■	■	I	■	H	■	K	■	■	■	M	■
S	T	A	R	E	■	H	E	A	R	S	A	Y
■	O	■	A	■	P	■	N	■	A	■	D	■
N	U	C	L	E	A	R	■	S	T	E	E	P
■	R	■	■	■	P	■	S	■	H	■	■	E
H	I	S	T	O	R	I	C	■	E	■	■	S
■	S	■	A	■	I	■	A	R	R	E	S	T
S	T	R	U	C	K	■	R	■	■	Y	■	L
■	S	■	T	■	A	N	Y	W	H	E	R	E

190

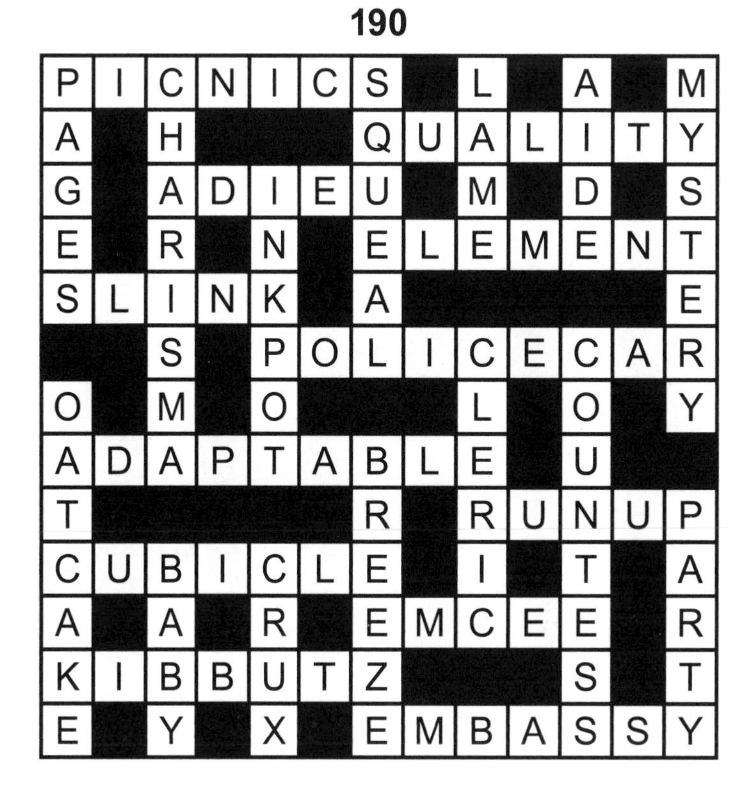

191

T	R	A	F	F	I	C	■	C	A	B	E	R
I	■	D	■	A	■	A	■	O	■	■	X	■
G	N	A	T	S	■	S	L	A	C	K	E	N
R	■	P	■	H	■	H	■	T	■	■	C	■
E	N	T	W	I	N	E	■	S	U	N	U	P
S	■	O	■	O	■	W	■	■	■	■	T	■
S	E	R	E	N	E	■	A	S	L	E	E	P
■	A	■	■	■	■	E	■	T	■	M	■	E
D	R	O	W	N	■	S	I	R	L	O	I	N
■	L	■	■	E	■	T	■	I	■	T	■	A
C	O	M	P	E	T	E	■	D	R	I	L	L
■	B	■	■	D	■	E	■	E	■	O	■	T
B	E	A	K	S	■	M	A	S	O	N	R	Y

192

Solutions

193

194

195

196

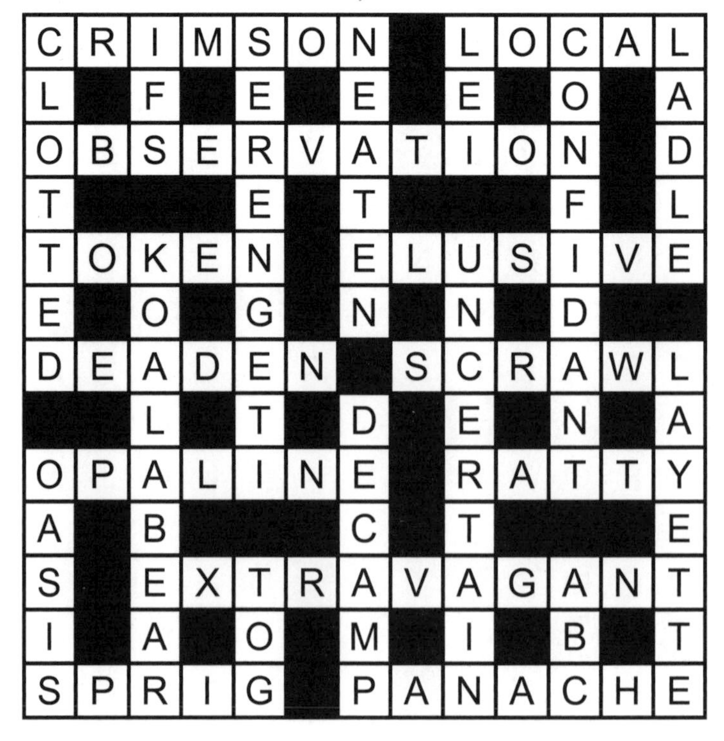

Solutions

197

M	I	S	T	A	K	E	N		A	S	K	S
E		N	A	P		D				H		I
A	R	E	N	A		I	C	E	L	A	N	D
T		E	G	R	E	T				M		E
		Z		T		O	I	L	W	E	L	L
W	H	E	T	H	E	R		I		D		I
I				E				S				N
Z		J		I		A	N	T	I	Q	U	E
A	B	A	N	D	O	N		E		U		
R		G				D	A	N	T	E		S
D	O	G	S	T	A	R		E	R	U	P	T
R		E				E		R	U	E		A
Y	A	R	N		P	A	S	S	E	D	B	Y

198

P	A	S	T	I	L	L	E		S	C	O	T
E		A		N		A		D		A		I
E	R	R	A	T	I	C		E	R	R	O	R
K		I		E		T		L		D		E
			A	R	T	I	F	I	C	I	A	L
G		I		M		C		C		N		E
R	A	N	G	E	R		H	A	R	A	S	S
A		V		D		S		T		L		S
P	R	I	V	I	L	E	G	E	D			
H		T		A		V		S		D		A
I	D	I	O	T		E	A	S	E	O	F	F
T		N		E		R		E		M		A
E	R	G	O		R	E	I	N	D	E	E	R

199

S	C	A	M	P		B			P		B	
E		F		A		A	C	C	L	A	I	M
R	E	F	I	N	E	R	Y		A		C	
G		O		E		S	L	I	T	H	E	R
E		R			D		I		Y		P	
A	D	D	I	T	I	O	N		P	U	S	S
N			D		S		D		U			E
T	H	E	E		P	H	E	A	S	A	N	T
	A		N		E		R			N		P
W	R	I	T	I	N	G		O		G		I
	D		I		S	A	P	P	H	I	R	E
S	E	T	T	L	E	S		U		N		C
	N		Y			H		S	C	A	L	E

200

Solutions

201

L		B		L		A	B	S	C	E	S	S
A	D	A	G	E		C		E		C		E
P		S		A	F	T	E	R	N	O	O	N
L	O	T	U	S		O		V		L		S
A		I		H	E	R	B	I	C	I	D	E
N		O				S		L			N	
D	Y	N	A	M	O		W	E	B	C	A	M
	A			O		I				Y		I
E	M	I	G	R	A	N	T	S		C		S
A		N		A		D		P	I	L	L	S
S	A	C	R	I	L	E	G	E		O		I
E		U		N		N		L	I	N	E	N
L	A	R	G	E	S	T		L		E		G